The
Road
to
Corbyn

G000160474

8

THE ROAD TO CORBYN
A MODERN-DAY PILGRIM'S PROGRESS

ROB DONOVAN

Matador
9 Priory Business Park,
Wistow Road, Kibworth Beauchamp,
Leicestershire. LE8 0RX
Tel: 0116 279 2299
Email: books@troubador.co.uk
Web: www.troubador.co.uk/matador
Twitter: @matadorbooks

ISBN 978 1785892 912

British Library Cataloguing in Publication Data.
A catalogue record for this book is available from the British Library.

Printed and bound by CPI Group (UK) Ltd, Croydon, CR0 4YY
Typeset in 11pt Minion Pro by Troubador Publishing Ltd, Leicester, UK

Matador is an imprint of Troubador Publishing Ltd

ACKNOWLEDGEMENTS

I would like to thank the members of the Reading Circle in the far south-west of Cornwall, in particular Clare Lynch, Pippa Stilwell, John Stilwell and Roy Phillips, whose helpful criticisms of the original text have played a vital part in the production of *The Road to Corbyn*.

I am also very grateful to Troubador/Matador Publishing who have been exemplary. My particular thanks to Lauren Lewis, Becky Millar, Rachel Gregory, Robert Warner, Alice Graham and Sian Orrell, all of whom have helped guide my work to publication. Finally, and not least, my thanks to my copyeditor, Faye L. Booth. Her expertise has been invaluable and spared me much heartache.

CONTENTS

An Introduction

One night, on my journey through the wilderness of this world, I laid me down to sleep and the likeness of a dream came to me, and behold, I saw men and women and children and they were all suffering.

From the shadows, a man emerged, bent double by the great burden on his back, and he cried out, "What shall I do?" And he began to sob. He was greatly distressed.

In my dream, I watched as a woman gowned in plain white cloth appeared at his side and spoke: "My name is Hope. You know me already. Why do you weep?"

The man bent double by the great burden on his back answered: "When I began to understand that I had an inner me, I was a child. Yet even then, I resolved to understand the world in which I lived. As I grew older I came to realise that all I did had consequences, and all that others did, likewise. I heard many stories about the good and the bad effects of people's actions. I became a seeker after truth, and my name became Pilgrim. I learnt about the visions for a better and kinder world in which people loved one another just as they would wish to be loved by others. But between the idea and the reality, there fell such a shadow."

"This is the story of the world so far," Hope replied. "Do you think this is the way the world ends too?"

"Perhaps. The more I know, the more overwhelming the issues facing us seem. My burden of fear and doubt grows ever heavier, the list of wrongs suffered, of cruelties inflicted, lengthens by the day. I feel I would be deceiving myself if I were to believe anything other than that the best I can hope for is the chance to sit still and lift the burden from my back."

"As a species you are prone to self-deception," Hope said. "I have observed that those who have power and wealth first deceive themselves in order to deceive those they wish to control. Perhaps you, Pilgrim, self-deceive to spare yourself the struggles in the journey ahead of you. But are you ready to abandon the quest for truth and understanding that filled your soul as a child?"

"Your rebuke is warranted," Pilgrim admitted. "But I have become exhausted as the years have passed, and the terrain seems harder. It is as if the world is turning in a new direction that is contrary to what I know would lead to a better age where every person mattered."

"Do not despair. I will show you a special path to take you further on your journey to find truth and understanding. When you need me, I will be there. But first, there is another companion for your journey whom you also know, and she too will be with you when you need her."

In my dream, I watched as Pilgrim rose and picked up his load. Hope remained close by his side. A solitary, bare tree marked the point where they had met. On a bough of this dying tree, there appeared a bird whose colours, crimson red and honey yellow, flamed in the sunlight as the creature swooped towards its perch. Pilgrim met the gaze of the bird, whose name was Charity. The bird spoke.

"You have known me in the past and I will not abandon you, now or ever. The Lady Hope and I will be with you when you need us on your special path – your journey to find truth and understanding."

And in my dream, Pilgrim was suddenly alone by the dying tree beside the dirt track. I watched him as he began to stride forward towards the fully risen sun, now magnificently red, over the horizon at the end of the path that stretched out ahead. Pilgrim's mission had begun.

Pilgrim Meets the Interpreter

In a small clearing in the wood that Pilgrim had entered a few minutes before, following the path down the valley towards the mass of verdant oak before him, he found the path now divided. The Lady Hope appeared beside him.

"Here at this crossroads your journey begins in earnest," she said. "From now to the end of your special path you will need not only the assurance of myself and Charity, but also another voice to guide you. He is the Interpreter. Ask and you will hear. Do not doubt the hearing. Whether you accept his account is for you to decide. He will explain more about your special path. All I will say is that you are being gifted an insight into the history of a relatively small island of which you already have some knowledge. But your journey is undertaken at a time when this island is home to around one in every hundred people who are alive today on your planet. You will see this island's tribal leaders warring with each other, using words as weapons. You will see a conflict of ideas that threaten my death and the extinction of Charity. This is a struggle with which you are already familiar, but you are being graced with a unique perspective as you follow your special path."

With these words, the Lady Hope fell silent and gently faded. Pilgrim felt the cloak of comfort fall over his shoulders. In my dream, I saw him look towards the fork in the path, undecided. Then it was as if I was Pilgrim, because I too could hear the voice in his head.

"I heard your call and I am here. My name is the Interpreter. I will show you those things that profit your soul and the lives of others, and those things that do not. In that lies my bias. The path you need to take is the one that leads to the most content for the many and the least misery for the few. Let me explain further."

And in my dream, I heard our world reduced to its simplicities.

We, as a species, have evolved from less complex organisms to a point at which it seems we control the world. Our capacity to think and to communicate our ideas, to solve problems that we encounter, to understand and use the elements of the natural world to our advantage, has led to us inhabiting the land on this planet, Earth, in ways which – for some – are ever more knowing. Through the work of those considered the cleverest people, systems of knowledge have been developed in the quite recent past, largely within the last 250 years, that have given members of the species this unprecedented control. These systems of knowledge are the sciences, such as physics and chemistry and engineering. They form worlds of interconnected ideas whose coherence depends on knowing that inside such worlds there will always be predictable outcomes. The application of this scientific knowledge has led to the development of ever more powerful technologies such as steam, electric, nuclear and digital that have transformed the way some of the species live.

Remarkably, and as a consequence of the transformation set in motion by these new technologies, the total number of our species has risen exponentially in this last quarter of a millennium to reach seven billion people. However, the species has become more divided in status than ever before. Most humans live in poverty, despite the new sciences and technologies. They have very little money, they eat just enough to live, perhaps half of them are often hungry, and hundreds and thousands of them actually die prematurely through starvation.

Yet a quarter of the species do not live in poverty. Their dwelling places are called, collectively, the 'developed world'. The others – the unfortunate and overwhelming majority who do live in poverty – dwell in what is called the 'developing world'. To be precise, since only a small fraction of the population in each country in the 'developing world' has a privileged access to that nation's wealth and power, the majority of people there do not experience a world that is developing in quite the way the adjective may suggest. And to be precise again, since there is also only a relatively small elite in each country in the 'developed world' who have a privileged access to that nation's wealth and power, most people there do not share fully in the fruits of development.

Hunger, starvation and premature death are not features of the 'developed world' by definition but – as the Interpreter took pains to emphasise – in the last forty years there has been a widening of inequalities in those largely northern hemisphere countries that make up the 'developed world'. For increasing numbers of people, there has been a reversal in the advances in living standards over the last two centuries that brought about the idea of a 'developed world' in the first place. The developed world is becoming more unequal too. [1]

The Interpreter paused at this point and looked at Pilgrim.

Could the explanation of the Interpreter in my dream be a deception? Was Pilgrim being fed a diet of lies and half-truths? So far all I had heard seemed factual and credible. The Interpreter's account of a world divided into unequal parts according to the distribution of knowledge, wealth and power had the ring of truth. His next chilling move was to show how this expansion in scientific understanding in the last quarter-millennium had brought such a degree of control over the forces of nature that humanity now had the means to wipe itself off the surface of the planet. Splitting atoms in missile weapon-heads could lead to a nuclear holocaust, destroying virtually all the higher life forms. Two such weapons had already been used in one world war, to devastating effect, at the very beginning of their scientific development, nearly seventy years ago over the centres of Hiroshima and Nagasaki.[2] Fifty years ago, the leaders of the two greatest national power blocs on the planet became locked in conflict over an island and nuclear war was as close as it has ever been.[3] 'Mutually assured destruction' became the grim name for safeguarding against the use of nuclear weapons, or MAD for short. Today, the pattern of international relations and hostilities has changed, but the stockpiles of nuclear weapons remain.

And these nuclear weapons seemed to be addictive. The Interpreter narrowed his focus and spoke specifically about that relatively small island in the developed world that the Lady Hope had said would be the place of Pilgrim's journey to find meaning and truth. It seemed that the political leaders of this island had been among the first to acquire these nuclear weapons, seventy or so years before. Now, faced with no apparent or likely nuclear threat from another nuclear-armed power, their leaders had decided to renew their nuclear weaponry at the cost of around £100 billion. This they had done at the very time when the country was recovering from an economic crisis that had almost bankrupted the state.[4] Even the Interpreter's calm and matter-of-fact tone seemed stretched at that point in his account.

It was not, however, only the particular advances in nuclear science and applied weapon technologies that threatened to destroy the species. The industrial revolutions that had followed the scientific discoveries and the technological innovations, first in the developed world and then in parts of the developing world, had led to what was now accepted by an overwhelming number of scientists as the phenomenon of global warming. The carbon emissions produced in the powering of industry had accumulated in the atmosphere to such an extent that they were affecting the natural mechanisms for deflecting the intensity of the sun's heat. For the first time, humanity had tilted the delicate balance that sustained its own life on Planet Earth to a point of disequilibrium. The planet was now become hotter, sea levels were rising as icecaps melted – and there was nothing that could be done to stop this; any actions now would only ameliorate these trends, although such actions in themselves were still crucial for the long-term preservation of our civilisations.[5]

The Interpreter's promise to provide an explanation reduced to its simplicities was being fulfilled, but the account was grim and becoming grimmer. Pilgrim remained motionless, seated on the grass by the edge of the dirt track under the wooden stake that marked the crossroads. Then I heard Pilgrim address the Interpreter:

"You tell of unbelievable and distressing matters that are far from my experience. Yet there is something about these stories that has the ring of truth. I cannot stop myself from wanting to hear more, but all I have heard only adds to my burden of exhaustion. What hope is there? Why should I continue my travels? Why should I proceed any further on this special path that seems to have been prepared for me?"

"My task is to provide an explanation for the shape of the world you will encounter on your journey if you choose to continue on this path," the Interpreter replied. "You have others who will help you answer such questions if you need such assistance. For now, remember the power of your own child-spirit."

Pilgrim rose from the ground, picked up his load and spoke. "I am by nature curious and at my best I believe in good outcomes. I will continue. I shall take the track that points to my left through the wood because my heart and head tell me to do so."

And Pilgrim marched forward.

It was not long before I saw in my dream that Pilgrim had entered a section of the wood in which the branches of the oaks had grown so close together that the path had become almost impenetrable. Pilgrim had no choice but to pause. I could feel the question addressed to the Interpreter forming in his mind even before Pilgrim spoke:

"You tell of a world shaped by industrial and market forces I can scarcely imagine, and you talk of leaders who have wealth and power and some measure of control in that world. I have some understanding of the dangers of wealth and power, but the paths I have taken in my past have been shaped by a vision of another, better world. I remember a celestial city ruled by a Lord who would free those who find themselves in bondage to sin and despair, and who are only worldly-wise. Is this journey I am now undertaking bound for that same city?" [6]

"My task is to explain only the things of this world as we find it now," said the Interpreter. "I will talk only of what we can reasonably know for sure through observation and enquiry, and not of those matters we may call issues of belief and faith. You have two guides who travel by the names of the Lady Hope and Charity. Yours will be a journey without the support of faith. To be precise, your support will come from your conviction that this journey is worthwhile in your own search to find meaning for yourself and your species in this world. Is that enough?"

Pilgrim thought in silence for a while and then bowed his head in acceptance.

"Now," the Interpreter continued, "you need to understand some ideas and words that have been developed to make sense of this world in which you find yourself. Some of these ideas and words are as slippery as eels. So beware! First, there is a word, an idea, which is a magic term. It can transform itself into its opposite in the hands of magicians who may themselves be unaware that there are forces controlling them. I am talking of the term democracy. I know you have some familiarity with the word. You understand that its origins date back to the world of the Greeks around two and a half thousand years ago. It means 'rule of the people', as opposed to its opposite, aristocracy: 'rule of the elite'. Again, you do not need me to tell you that nothing vexes your species quite like the issue of rule. 'Who should rule me?' 'Who follows my rule?' When I offer you my explanation for why these eels are so slippery, always bear in mind that it is the issue of ruling which defines these matters: to whom do I give, to whom do I entrust my body and self? Or, more often, to whom do I find myself obliged, under whose rule do I suffer? You may remember that your last special journey took place in a century of revolution. A civil war was fought in which a very small group of radical thinkers set up a democratic state in a community on a hillside and recalled the words of a priest some three hundred years before: 'When Adam delved and Eve span/Who was then the gentleman?' [7] Neither you nor your countrymen then were very keen on such ideas of worldly equality. Perhaps that is why you followed a belief that turned things inside out so that we all became equal in an imagined world?" [8]

Pilgrim remained silent. The Interpreter continued.

"Be that as it may, in the course of the next three to four hundred years those who held power and wealth in this and other nations found themselves challenged by those they ruled. More and more, these challenges were in the name of democracy, in the name of the people. At first, only the most powerful and wealthy of the people who had been excluded from ruling succeeded in these attempts to join the ranks of the few who governed the state. But then the idea that defines democracy today gathered pace. Democracy became the ideal form of government, in which all eligible citizens were able to elect representatives who would act in their interests in making laws and carrying out the government. Political parties were developed that carried the flag for different opinions about how society should be ruled. Those who were eligible voted to choose their representatives in government, and these representatives were usually members of one or another of these political parties. All those who were ruled, the people, could feel content because they had used a vote to choose their rulers. Having a vote and valuing democracy became the hallmark of those who now believed they were no longer living in an unequal society.

"But who was eligible to vote? The people, of course – but the definition of the people excluded masses of people at the beginning of this movement for democracy. Those who were not regarded as competent adults could not have a vote. Slaves, children, those who had little or no property, women – all were initially excluded. It took many years and much conflict before those who held the power and wealth granted the vote to all men and women over the age of eighteen in the nations of the developed world." [9]

The Interpreter paused and then turned full-face to Pilgrim and asked, "Do you think you will find the people are now the rulers? Will they determine who rules them because they are able to cast a vote?"

"We will see," said Pilgrim. "But from what you say I think that this idea of democracy has been used by those who were excluded from the world of politics, to gain admission. And it seems to me that those who hold wealth and power in this world were forced through conflict and the fear of social unrest to widen the ranks of those within their political nation in the name of this idea called democracy. But I would be surprised if most of the wealth and power did not remain in the hands of the few. This, from my experience, is how it has always been."

"Let me introduce you to two other words, political terms that may deepen your grasp even further," the Interpreter added. "They also have Greek roots. You talk of power being held still by only a few people. Well, the political system where power – and usually wealth too – is held by only a few people is known as an oligarchy. If power is held exclusively by the wealthy to serve their own purposes, then that system has become known as a plutocracy. This system of plutocracy has generally been regarded as a bad thing. Poverty increases and society becomes corrupted by greed. To date, a number of critics have gone as far as identifying the most powerful developed country – not your rather small island, although there are links – as both an oligarchy and a plutocracy in which democracy survives as little more than a smokescreen behind which the most wealthy and powerful set in motion forces that manipulate the masses into a state of collective ignorance of what is really shaping their world.[10] Democracy has been defined in the past as government of the people, by the people, for the people.[11] One thinker has rather aptly described the world of your powerful neighbour as government of the 1%, by the 1%, for the 1%.[12] Another thinker has estimated that in its population– which is five times bigger than yours – the bottom 70% on the wealth/income scale have really no influence in shaping their society whatsoever. Indeed, this thinker has said that it is only when you get to the very top, to the richest of all, the one tenth of 1% of the population, that you find the people who get what they want and determine the politics of making money.[13] It would be surprising if your land too was not ripe for much the same judgement."

Pilgrim had rested his back, leaning against the trunk of a tree, his load on the ground. He shook his head.

"I am not used to thinking in numbers such as these. The world seems so much more measured than I remember it. But there are limits to this calculation. Even those 1% – or one-tenth of 1% depending on how you measure it – will not always be able to have things all their own way. Total control never seems to me to have lasted for very long. In my experience, on my journeys, there is always space for the slip, for the incalculable, for the accident. Human beings do not always get it right. More often than not, the reverse is true. You talked before of something called global warming that humans have produced through their industrial revolutions. You said that humans could now only soften its impact but not prevent it altering the quality of life for future generations. You talked of a new power called nuclear, and it seemed clear to me that humans are now handling a fire that could wipe them out. How do the richest and most powerful make sense of such fears and the knowledge that not everything can be controlled? Do you think they understand their limitations?"

"When this journey began and the Lady Hope appeared by your side, she spoke of deception," said the Interpreter. "She offered you the idea that those who seek to control you through deception and manipulation must first deceive themselves. She is truly the Lady Hope because she not only understands this truth about human nature, but she also believes there is still a truth beyond deception. No, I do not think the richest and most powerful understand their limitations. They deceive themselves that the control they enjoy now will last forever. It is as if they are in love with the market forces that have shaped the circumstances that have led to their wealth and power. They trust that one way or another those market forces will always favour them because they are the natural leaders of the world."

"You speak of market forces… It is a term with which I am unfamiliar," Pilgrim admitted.

"The idea of the market is one I know that you understand. Quite soon in their history, human beings began to buy from each other the things they needed but could not themselves grow or make. Humans became buyers and sellers in the marketplace. Soon the market became a place where humans sold their own labour to others for a price. Money was minted to make this buying and selling more straightforward. Humans worked for others to make or grow things and were paid with money, which meant they could go back to the market to buy what they needed. A new force had now entered the world. People began to realise that a profit could be made from such market deals. More money could be made from making sure that the deal was fixed to your advantage. Money and power became inextricably linked. Power was needed to gain the advantage; money helped ensure you had the power. The industrial revolution, which I have already explained, accelerated these market forces in a way that humans have not yet fully grasped. Now there is a marketplace that fills the whole world, a global economy in which those who have fallen in love with money invent ways to make more money, more profit. Money can be made from money. It is commercial alchemy. Every activity, every transaction between humans, can potentially become part of this market.[14] You will see much of this on your journey."

"But surely these market forces will mean your developed world will always seek to have the advantage over the developing world? And won't the rich and powerful always be striving to keep their wealth and their status at the expense of those who have less?"

"You have already begun to draw your own conclusions about how far the few who have wealth shape what is called democracy. As you consider these matters, remember those things I have explained about oligarchy and plutocracy. Remember also the struggles I mentioned that had to be fought to secure the right to vote in elections for those who were disadvantaged. Wealth and power have been successfully challenged. Market forces have been regulated by elected representatives of people who used their vote to choose governments that did reduce the degree of inequality between fellow human beings…" [15]

The Interpreter paused. In my dream, his words were left suspended in the stillness of my night-world. I wanted to hear more, but I knew I was overcome by the sheer magnitude of what had been explained so far. But Pilgrim rose from the ground and bent down to pick up his burden. As he did so, the boughs that reached around him from all sides seemed to withdraw, and the overgrown and engulfing mass of branches and foliage around him retreated. The path became distinct. The way ahead through the wood was clear.

PILGRIM GOES TO THE ELECTION FAIR

It was now midday. The heat of early summer lay all around like a light enchantment as Pilgrim made his way boldly along the road that ran straight ahead, through the landscape of fields and woods and pasture, crossing streams by fords, a river by bridge. He remembered waiting at the crossroads, and the time he had seemed trapped in the forest by the boughs and foliage wrapping themselves around him. He could still hear the Interpreter's words and feel the sense of being uplifted by a new understanding. He remembered making a decision to pick up his load and move on. But there was no longer a memory of time passing, as he had once known.

Pilgrim became aware that an arch had appeared ahead of him, across the road. The arch was festooned with posters and helium party balloons in a variety of colours, and there was a hubbub of noise and commotion coming from the barely visible loudspeakers attached to the tall columns that formed the pillars of the arch. As he drew nearer, the tumult rose in volume. He felt giddy. Balloons began to burst and the heat became unnaturally intense, the air drier and hotter. Figures appeared on either side of him, behind and in front, leaping, clutching, imploring. He was being spun round, and around, and around. The arch was still there, across the road, but now the scene was transforming and I watched as

14

Pilgrim found himself flung across the back of a racing horse that stared ahead at the flying tail of another bolting steed. He was going round and round and round.

The Election Fair had arrived, and victory was the toast of the day.

Pilgrim had not enjoyed the indignity of being a passenger on a meteoric magic roundabout, conjured up by a wizard of unknown intent. He did, nevertheless, have some grasp of what had happened. The Lady Hope had warned him that there would be moments of testing on his journey in search of truth. He must have passed through the archway that marked an election victory and found himself in this celebratory fair. Pilgrim could feel the sense of a past recalled sweep through him. Another journey, another place, another fair... Souls sold for commercial gain... The merchandising of every human activity and all things... A fair dating back to the beginning of time and ruled by Mammon, the grasping figure of greed who controlled the human species through love of money. Vanity Fair. [16]

Rows and streets, as in other fairs, named after the commodities to be sold there. Here is the Health Row, the Education Row, the Postal Services Row – in every row, stall after stall after stall, crammed with goods. The hoardings screamed their messages above the hubbub of traders: *Make your profit now – Buy while you can – Don't delay, buy today.*

Pilgrim lurched back from the thrusting hands that sought to pull him towards their row, their stalls. All around him were well-fleshed figures whose bodily form shrank and swelled, as in a room of glass mirrors. Pilgrim felt himself drowning in a sea of lusting humanity, disembodied by their own avarice. He could smell the sweat and piss and shit.

The next moment he was shoved by the heaving mass into the entrance of a small marquee in the very centre of all the commotion. But the moment he found himself inside, all the noise and mayhem evaporated. Here, the air was refreshing and cool. A man in his late thirties, tanned and athletically elegant, dressed in the smart-casual style that I recognised in my dream as a fashion of my own time, sat behind a desk, smiling.

"You must pardon the enthusiasm of the traders. Sometimes the excitement of the dealing becomes rather too excessive for some tastes. Will you sit down for a moment or two? Take the weight off your legs, as they say."

The man continued smiling, his eyes fixed on Pilgrim. Watching them, I could feel the shudder in my own stomach as Pilgrim reached for the burden he carried on his back and found it was gone.

"Have you lost something?" Still smiling. "These crowds… You can never be too careful. Still, you looked rather uncomfortable carrying that great bag on your back." No explanations. Still the smile. "Better off without it, I expect."

There was a pause. Pilgrim could say nothing. He felt bereft. He had failed. He had let his burden slide from him and he had betrayed his journey to find the truth.

"You look confused. Please don't be. Enjoy this delightful space we have created here and rest assured that once you know how these things work, you too will never have to suffer inconvenience ever again. I can see you are a man of intent. We believe in looking after those who are special. We know you will bring great value to our business. We want you to be one with us…" He paused. "Indeed, one *of* us."

The syllables of the last three words lay like a trapped echo in the quiet of the space around him. Pilgrim realised for the first time that the room was air-conditioned.

"Let me explain how our market works, our wonderful fair – this fair you have called Vanity. I am afraid you have missed the mark there. There is nothing empty about our trading. There is something for everyone here. It is true that some will make more than others, receive more for their contribution than others, but that is only as it should be since their input is more valuable, their skills more precious. They have more understanding of how our market works best. That's why they are one with us. All of us – in this together. Remember, you can be one of us, one of the very special people who drive this market economy that brings wealth and happiness to all who recognise its value and are prepared to work hard and use their God-given skills for the benefit of themselves and their families."

The smile remained even as he continued. "Of course, there are those who paint a different picture. I know they have tried to influence you. They have told you of inequalities. They complain of suffering. I believe they may have been responsible for your distress and your decision to take up your load again and set out on another of your journeys…"

He paused. "It is all so unnecessary. I feel for you, I really do. You have a good heart. Your intentions are, shall we say, noble? Just cast your mind back to the time before this, when you made your journey in search of a celestial city. My concern here is not with the truth or otherwise of what you discovered on that mission but with what you remember of the well-being of the people you encountered. For a moment, compare the age and health and prosperity of the mass of the people then and what you have seen around you in your journey to date."

Pilgrim felt his ease now the load had been removed from his back; the comfort and the stillness and peace of the room in which he found himself. This man sitting opposite him behind the desk had an aura of calm confidence. His words were unlocking buried memories for Pilgrim, opening up glimpses of a past time. Images, floating and merging and separating out... the surreal confusion of experiencing at first hand the realities of living beings separated by hundreds of years of development.

Development... that had been the idea that had come naturally to him as he tried to make sense of his thoughts. It was true that the masses he had encountered at the Election Fair were different from the masses he now remembered from another journey.

The man behind the desk spoke again. "You are beginning to see a different picture, aren't you? Trust me. You are not mistaken. Take any ordinary person you met on the journey you undertook before the time of industrial revolution. Give them the insight into the future that you now have and ask them which time they would rather live in. Would you expect the Good Lord that you worshipped to be angry that a humanity that was made in his image should today be living longer, suffering less disease, enjoying more reward for their labours? Ask the question in the developed world; ask the question in the developing world. I think you know how most ordinary, decent, fair-minded people will answer, wherever they come from. One would be a fool not to want a better quality of life."

The smile thickened. "My friend, do not trust those who want to stir up trouble, those who want to rock the boat. There will always be spoilers, men and women with issues. They cannot, will not, see the bigger picture. You and I have the vision and the intellect to know that all this prosperity and well-being, all this development, is due to the work of an ever-developing, ever more global market. There are some who fall by the wayside for a time, but in the end it is up to the individual whether he picks himself up or not. Isn't that so?"

Pilgrim sat silently in the chair. A great comfort, even tenderness, was enveloping him. The man behind the desk had spoken and his words were like drops of manna in the desert of his soul. Pilgrim was being graced with a way of seeing the world in a new light. Before, there had been only misery and poverty and unhappiness. But that was the old order. That was how things had always been. Now there really was change for the better. He could see it. For the first time. A world that had developed a way for making life better for more and more people. Its leaders deserved praise, not blame.

Pilgrim did not remember seeing the man move from behind the desk, but there he was on the far side of the room, drawing open a velvet curtain to reveal the open doors of what seemed to be another very small room.

"I think your journey is over."

The man stood tall and confident, his smile reassuring.

"You have found your truth. It is, so to speak, the only truth. Come. This elevator will take us together to the real centre of our world. Our headquarters. Where we control matters."

Pilgrim found himself only a few feet away from his guide and the open doors. He could smell his new companion's freshness. He knew that this guide knew every thought that passed through Pilgrim's mind.

At that moment, the sweep of crimson red and honey yellow filled the space around them and a new sound filled the air, so wonderful that Pilgrim could feel his soul soaring. The room was now infused with crimson and honey, the essence of the bird-creature that had promised never to abandon Pilgrim. The tiny creature was transformed. A bird call sounded so sublime that Pilgrim shivered with delight, and in my dream I saw Pilgrim's would-be guide fade into oblivion. Charity said nothing. There was no need. Her call had been beyond words.

Pilgrim Enters the Free Market Inn

Pilgrim looked around. The room, the elevator, the man – all had gone. On his back, there was a familiar feeling. Behind him, some distance away, he could see the arch across the path and the sprawl of the Election Fair stretching towards the horizon. Ahead, clouds were gathering over a point on the horizon where he could just make out the outlines of a wayside building. For a moment, the burden he carried felt heavier, but then he knew the Lady Hope was beside him and the load eased.

"I have kept my promise too," said Hope. "When you need me, I will be there. What you have been through was difficult, but there will be other encounters on this journey when you will need both Charity and myself. You have survived a meeting with the force that controls the Vanity Fair that lies behind us. But do not think you can ever free yourself from that market. It will always be around you on your journey. I will help bring you the strength you will need to follow this path through to the end. I am the Lady Hope. But only at the end of the journey will we know if your progress has met with election success. Neither I nor Charity know that outcome for sure. It may be that the lord of Vanity Fair, the master of global market forces as he describes himself, will yet prove the victor. But your journey will not have been in vain. We believe that he can be controlled, even if he is beyond elimination. Our strength is superior to his, but at the same time it is more fragile…"

The Lady Hope, in her simple white gown, looked ahead, resolute but sad.

"These are not easy matters. But for you to succeed you must believe that your journey will be worthwhile and your victory assured. You have witnessed at first hand his power to deceive. You must remember that Charity was able to overcome even that awesome power. Mammon melted even as he thought he had you for the taking. Remember. He can be controlled."

The clouds darkened further as they drew nearer to the wayside building. It was a hotel of sorts, its sign neon-lit, announcing to any passer-by its primary provenance and purpose: The Free Market Inn.

"Here I must leave you to find your own way forward," Hope said. "We have prepared you as far as we are able. When you need support, listen. The Interpreter will ensure that justice is observed in the accounting."

The next moment, Pilgrim found himself inside the Free Market Inn and approaching the bar. He had never seen a building like this before. There were no hand-pumps or drinking-glasses or bottles to be seen; no signs of its function as an inn; no customers; no sound to be heard. But all was glass. Glass mirror-walls reflecting back his own figure as he eased the burden from his back; opaque glass doors, all shut; glass-covered hoardings mounted on glass screens displaying a bewildering medley of goods, the like of which Pilgrim had never seen before. Above the bar, a mammoth-sized glass screen was split into sections; as if by magic, each filled with images of human forms moving to and fro against a background of buildings. They were pictures from a town, he was certain at least of that. And a very busy town. As he stared in fascination at the multiple images produced by a dozen or so webcams positioned across the centre of the capital of this island on which he now found himself, Pilgrim experienced a shivery feeling that he might have some dim remembrance of some of these scenes. But so much had changed. So much was new.

Pilgrim blinked. A human figure was behind the bar. Pilgrim was certain the room had been empty. The barman, if that was who he was, seemed at first glance very young, a diminutive figure. His head and shoulders and not much else leaned towards Pilgrim over the bar, beckoning him forward. The barman, or the barman's son perhaps, smiled. Pilgrim had seen a smile like that before. It was wise to be cautious. Pilgrim's hand tightened over the straps of the load resting against his leg.

"Welcome to the Free Market Inn, Pilgrim. We have been expecting you. I am the keeper of the books here, the barkeeper if you will. I see to the figures. The Team call me Pocket Money. It's our little joke. It makes us feel more human."

He giggled. The sound was too high-pitched to qualify for a laugh.

"Now, where was I? Yes, the Team. You'll be wanting to know about the Team at some point, if you aren't already. Historians will in the future, I'm sure, but that's too much information."

The giggle again.

"My line manager – pardon me, I am forgetting your understandable ignorance – I mean the person, the man, who is in fact your host at this inn, my boss, if you like – he who is none other than Head Boy himself, the leader of the land…"

He leant further forward so his forehead almost touched the glass counter, and he had to turn his face sideways for the words to squeeze out.

"I say my boss, but between the two of us, speaking, as it were, to one who I am sure will soon be happy to consider himself almost as one of the Team, he and I go back a long way together. The punters…" his hands shot up, gesticulating towards the webcam images of urban humanity above him, his face still sideways, eyes fixed on Pilgrim "…need their hierarchies. So for them, he is the line manager. But believe me, we are a team, the two of us. We learnt to play together; we shared the same schooling."

He paused and straightened. He glanced towards one of the closed doors.

"We have another member of the Team. He is in our team because we need him and he needs us. He likes being in our team. He has never been so important. He likes to think he shares our views on some things. But I fear he is prone to self-deception. You won't be hearing much of him."

The smile again.

"You see we know what we're up to, Head Boy and I. We don't do self-deception. That's why it's such a fun game. Ah! Here is the man himself, or should I say boy?" The giggle again, even more high-pitched. Then another voice, another sound – somewhere else in the room; the tone, a showman's sweeping cadenza.

It's your celebrity host, your team-leader – parrrr… exxxx…cellll…enceeee! From the screen above the bar, until now soundless, there suddenly burst forth from the direction of the masses swirling around in the multiple images the resounding, chanted echo of the celebrity host's journey into a foreign language.

Parrrr...exxxx...cellll...enceeee! It reminded Pilgrim of a party game he had known as a child.

Pilgrim was about to speak when he realised that Pocket Money had slipped from sight and the images on the screen had switched to a single shot of a smooth, pink and rather fleshy face, apparently disembodied, repeated multiple times across the landscape of the big screen. Was this the face of Head Boy? Was he the celebrity host? Was he really the team leader too? Were all three one and the same? The Head Boy, the celebrity host, the team leader – one being; three personae.

The questions were scarcely formed when the screen images flickered and morphed into one reassuring close-up of that benign and smiling face.

"I speak to you today as the leader of this great country..."

So this was indeed Head Boy. Pilgrim listened intently, still standing, still clutching the straps of his load.

"...The leader of a coalition of forces that will now, after this election victory, restore all our fortunes and deliver us from the misfortunes bequeathed to us by the excesses of the last government. We will take the burden from your shoulders. United we will pay off the debts you have incurred thanks to the incompetence of those you unknowingly trusted with your democratic mandate. We will cut back the role of the state. We will then reduce taxation. We know that public services fail. We all see private enterprise works better, more efficiently. People become richer when the state does not interfere. Let the market find its natural level. Let's stop getting in the way. Nurture growth. Reward endeavour. Our promise is to cut out waste, encourage the hardworking – and take out the wasters. All the scroungers and skivers and benefit cheats had better look out! There is a new way in town. It's our way. The way of the hardworking majority who are overburdened and overtaxed and leeched on by those I am not afraid to name as welfare parasites. We have an enemy in our midst, a peril that must be extinguished…"

The team leader had paused. Pilgrim wondered whether he was going to identify him, Pilgrim, by name, live on air, as an enemy of the state.

"We – my team and I – have a solution. We will begin today as we mean to go on. Our way is straightforward. We mean business. It's game on."

The screen morphed back into multiple images of stamping, waving, cheering, flag-waving masses. The bar had become a cinema with an audience of one.

PILGRIM ENCOUNTERS POSTMUTIN

Pilgrim felt a hand brush his shoulder and knew that the Interpreter was beside him, even as the scenes of inn and bar and cinema faded and he found himself back on the dirt track, walking forward along the path across a valley floor, a stream beside him, his load intact on a back still straight.

"Well... what made you of the thoughts of our putative Head Boy and his sidekick Pocket Money?" the Interpreter asked.

Pilgrim looked surprised. He had not expected a remark so pointed.

"I promised to show you those things that profit your soul and the lives of others. In that intent lies my bias," explained the Interpreter. "Do not be surprised when I show my allegiance. In the end, there are always sides to favour, sides to resist. Come, let us rest here and I will explain more."

They settled together on a mound beside the stream. Pilgrim loved this landscape, this natural world: water, air, earth; the scents, the sounds of birds, the colours of corn and wild flowers and grasses. The glimpses of hordes of humanity had left him unsettled. Here, there was no human movement other than his own progress. He was moving through a landscape shaped by human hands, but now devoid of any human presence other than himself and his Interpreter. He realised he was already taking the Interpreter to his heart.

"When Head Boy spoke, his words spun round in my head and left a feeling of warmth and well-being," Pilgrim said. "It was as if I was back at Vanity Fair and listening to Mammon himself before the moment Charity arrived and rescued me. Why is it that I fall under the spell of these words and thoughts so easily?"

"These words and thoughts are spun with care and devotion. They are meant to take you in, to ensnare you, to make you one with them. The spinners of these words and thoughts are master craftsmen. Their lives, their beings are dedicated to what they see as truth. Remember, to achieve the perfect deception, there must first be complete self-deception. There is, though, an exception to this rule of thumb – there are now some who are more knowing about their own roles as deceivers and even self-deceivers. I will name them as they, in private, name themselves: political gamesters of the postmodernist kind. Let me explain further and then you must decide for yourself how self-knowing the spinners of deception are whom you encounter on the journey."

The Interpreter's hand reached out from his gown and pointed towards the darkening east. The day was drawing to a close but Pilgrim knew that these glimpses of a time passing were from another age. Here there was no time as he had once known it, only a journey and a search for understanding.

"There is a land thousands of miles away over those hills that has a part to play in our story," the Interpreter explained. "Once it was ruled by those who claimed they governed for the people. Across the world, many who believed in justice and equality, liberty and fairness, took this land and this government as their inspiration and their exemplar. This was a land that cried out that they had rooted out the evils of rampant market forces; they had tamed what was now termed by all sides as capitalism – the market forces whose energies derived from the drive to make profit through the making and exchange of goods. Unfortunately, this was a land that cried out for other reasons – deeds were done that bore witness to the disease of the new rulers. For a time, there was in effect only one leader. It was a land of huge resources and energy, and so it became one of the two superpowers of the planet. But in the course of history, corruption and the disease of power rotted away the fabric of whatever remained of its new democratic ideals. Until one day, only a generation ago in your time, those who governed simply gave up. They withered away. And what was left amongst the debris and remaking was a new state ruled by forces that have a showman as their representative, and he has his own puppeteer pulling the strings that keep the show onstage. The man in charge is known as Postmutin, his puppeteer, Vladi Onkov. I will take you inside their theatre if you wish." [17]

Pilgrim nodded. The next moment, the mound had dissolved and Pilgrim was watching a well-muscled body-builder, wearing only training paints, bestriding a stage from one side to the other, flexing to the left, flexing to the right, with a living backcloth of gyrating showgirls behind him. And he was singing. Pilgrim found he understood the words as they were delivered.

I am the very model of a modern Super Status Man,
I've information, malleable, censored and 'lectronic,
I know the ways of governing and democratic servitude

And I've got my puppetmaster, Vladi Onkov is his name.

PR's the way, TV's the means; our land's a propaganda game,

The state's so rotten, we know that truth: power's a thing most precious,

We live it up and take our chances; we are just so audacious.

We've put the land to service on a platform most postmodernist

And sad to tell but sure as hell, we'll have your details on our list. [18]

Pilgrim listened as the unseen audience roared their approval in choruses of rapturous applause.

"Do you follow, Pilgrim?" the Interpreter asked. "Their leader is one with them, a man of the people. He has the people behind him, at least enough of them to ensure his hold on power for the present. It matters less what he is saying and much more how he is conveying his truth. They are enjoying the spectacle. They want to be like him, they want the taste of power. It's not their details but the details of the opposition they care about, those who stand in the way of their own advancement, those who are not one with them, who are not of them, I mean the scapegoated, the soon to be beaten up, jailed, disappeared, broken... Postmutin and his kind use the people who vote for them, but it is a symbiotic connection. They are using his power to develop their own in their communities, their strongholds of power. The showman's understanding – politics as a postmodernist game – belongs to a man born in the 50s, a child of the 60s. And remember: Head Boy emerged in the next decade here in this land, with Pocket Money, five years his junior, following just after. But their love of power crosses the generations; that lust and delight is eternal."

"Your explanations are grim, said Pilgrim. "There was a time when I remember finding comfort in a faith that there would be a better, kinder world after our time of suffering here was over. I have not heard much of such a belief on this journey and doubt if I will. The masses seem to put their faith elsewhere in these times."

"It is true. Those who enjoy power in the state rely less on religious faith these days in their pursuit of wealth and status. There are other more immediately enticing devices to win the people over. What religion has to offer is on the whole too long-term for today's tastes."

"But I still have Hope and Charity?"

"You do. Come. It's time to resume your journey. Follow the stream to the bottom of the valley and you will see the track runs past a bridge that crosses the stream. The bridge looks safe but you will see signs of recent repair. Do not trust it. Do not cross over to the cottage on the other side. Stop and wait. Remember, time may not pass in a customary way here in this land. A figure will emerge from the cottage. You will see from your side of the riverbank that the cottage is called Well-Being. The figure will stride towards you and stop when he reaches the bridge. He will beckon you across. Do not, on any account, step forward onto the bridge. He may name himself in a variety of forms and all of them will sound good. He is a seducer of souls. Beware. He is a figure whose real name is No Benefit. Listen to what he has to say. Think about all you have learned to date and make your own assessment. But do nothing. Stay on your side of the stream. When the time is right I will say what needs to be said."

Pilgrim Meets No Benefit

And so it happened. Pilgrim followed the path to the bottom of the valley, stopped at the bridge and looked towards the cottage, thinking how attractive it seemed, with smoke rising from its chimneys and an open stable-type front door offering a glimpse of upholstered comfort within. A figure emerged, a prosperous man – the local squire, perhaps; a landowner, certainly. He was dressed as a rural gentleman would be, in tweeds and green boots, and in one hand, a polished ebony walking stick. In my dream, I shared Pilgrim's thought and shudder: this was indeed No Benefit, in person.

"Welcome to our land, dear Pilgrim," he cried. "The word has spread. 'A seeker of truth is coming your way.' I heard the message announced and was ready to greet you. It seems that not all you have heard to date has convinced you of the merits of a leaner and tougher government of our realm. Allow me to show you how far the rot has set in, how far the very foundations of our civilised society have been attacked by the fungus of empty lives, drained of meaning. I have such pride in being a member of our team. A force dedicated to bringing back physical health and spiritual meaning to millions of ordinary people who have been allowed to waste their lives. All this, through misgovernment in the past, in the name of Welfare. Millions – no, billions – of pounds of taxpayers' money have been eaten up by a profligate state over more than half a century in a corrosive attack on the liberty of the individual. In the name of do-goodery, the state has taken over the very souls of millions of its citizens, leaving them marooned on the sofas of their discontent, incapable of gaining mastery over their own lives…"

No Benefit interrupted himself. "Forgive my rudeness, Pilgrim. Come across to my cottage and rest for a while. There we can talk further on these matters that touch us so profoundly. Time can pass quite unexpectedly in these lands, and you may glimpse a future to thrill you."

Pilgrim remembered the warning. "It is better that we remain as we are. You on your side of the stream; I on my side. At least for the time being. Your words are spoken with force and clarity. I hear you well and am considering what you have to say. But it is better that I learn at a distance. I am finding this to be the case more and more as I reflect on these matters and consider the dangers of deception."

No Benefit's cheeks reddened with annoyance. He did not like to be crossed.

"I was told you would not be straightforward. There are forces at work here that I do not like. I sense there is something afoot that must be resisted by all those of good heart and conscience." The walking stick moved with intent, from hand to hand, scraping a rhythm on the gravel of the path beneath his feet.

"But who am I to question those more knowing than I?"

No Benefit's tone had lightened. He had made peace with himself and was resolved to continue carrying out his orders. "Very well! Stay there if you must, although the hospitality of this family estate is renowned throughout the district. Listen a while as I explain what we have done to put right the harm, yes, the evil, done by others."

And No Benefit spoke of the future, his words addressed to Pilgrim in a speech tailored for him and any other doubters who might care enough to listen.

"We have – since our election – pursued one of the most aggressive programmes of welfare reform that this land has ever seen. And we already have a proud record of achievement. There is no doubt that changes to the welfare state were and still are desperately needed. Our reforms will put an end to people being left on sickness benefit year after year. They will eradicate the trap that has left so many better off on benefits than in work. They will ensure the cost of benefits stays within reasonable and affordable limits."

No Benefit had struck a pose, an orator in declamatory mode, stick as baton beating time, his bare hand sweeping through crescendos.

"We promised a cap on benefits. We have delivered. We promised a universal credit framework to bring all benefits and tax credits into one system, and we are delivering, carefully and steadily. No rushed and botched job here. Have you not yet discovered on your journey the fact that there are scores of thousands of people in this land suffering the waste of long-term unemployment, trapped in idleness and a burden on all of us, the taxpayers who fund their welfare payments? I won't take lessons from those who, when in government, brought tax credit chaos and oversaw the decay of the welfare system."

Then the climax.

"We have made £83 billion of welfare savings. Those who oppose us let the rot set in when they were in government, and I am now busy putting things right. We are overseeing the making of a welfare state that is fair to both the people who use it and the taxpayers who pay for it." [19]

No Benefit had finished. He smiled benignly. Pilgrim gave a slight bow and spoke.

"I thank you for your words of explanation. You seem to have given much thought to these matters. I have a hint in my memory from other journeys of the pain of being out of work and watching others suffering that fate. If your schemes can lead to work for all, they must be welcomed by everyone. Are they not?"

"Not by all," No Benefit admitted. "But there are those who will oppose for the sake of opposition."

"But those who are being helped back into work – are they not grateful for your work?"

No Benefit said nothing in reply for a few seconds. Then he smiled and beckoned Pilgrim forward.

"They will be. One day. Come, Pilgrim, you really must return my favour. I have told you of my work. Now, please, the least you can do is accept my invitation to cross this bridge and join me for tea in the cottage of Well-Being."

Pilgrim tensed. By now, he knew these moments of testing. He was feeling increasingly confident that he could resist, unassisted.

"But I must still decline. For the present. There may be an opportunity later in my journey, but first I need to understand much more than I do now."

Pilgrim turned away from No Benefit and started on the path that led up the other side of the valley. He did not look back to see the figure in tweeds and boots storming back into the cottage, thrashing the air with his polished ebony stick.

PILGRIM LEARNS ABOUT IGNORANCE AND ECONOMICS

It was nightfall. Pilgrim had come to a halt on a section of the path that ran beside woodland on one side and on the other side, open fields reaching down to the river. The darkness of the wood was not inviting. As Pilgrim hesitated, uncertain, the next moment he knew the Interpreter was beside him.

"I need to explain, as simply as possible, more about these matters that you have encountered so far on your journey," the Interpreter said. "Come, I know this land. There is a cabin that lies some distance from this path, deeper in the wood. It is one of my safer houses…"

The Interpreter remained almost as expressionless as ever, but Pilgrim wondered if he had not caught a glimpse of concern.

"We need to move as quickly as we can through this wood until we reach our destination. Follow close behind me. No word must pass our lips. Do not fear the sights you see. As long as I am with you in the wood, you will remain free from harm. But remember. Do not fall behind. And close your mind to any thought other than the truth that we will soon be in a safe place."

Pilgrim remembered little of the swift passage along unseen tracks, following on the heels of the black-gowned figure striding ahead of him, other than grim, relentless fear. A myriad cluster of threatening eyes, like tiny, spherical planets lit in sulphur-yellow light, seemed to follow their movement through the wood in a canvas of pitch-dark night.

The Interpreter closed and locked the door of the cabin quietly. "Here we are free from their surveillance. But in this new world of exponential change, the digital revolution makes it more difficult than it used to be to avoid being overseen or overheard. [20] But our thoughts, at least, they cannot yet monitor, and tonight we have found our sanctuary. We will share food first – then my version of events for you to hear and assess."

And so the Interpreter began his account.

"I shall begin like a surgeon by cutting to the point of the problem that faces humankind in both the developed and developing worlds. Once you understand this issue, you will be better able to appreciate the webs of political rhetoric and self-deception that you have encountered so far on your journey."

Pilgrim looked across the table towards his guide. He knew that he trusted the Interpreter, but the matter of self-deception still lay on the table, ripe for further examination. How far did that web extend? Were its threads visible even in the space around them?

The Interpreter continued, as if attuned to Pilgrim's thoughts.

"Self-deception we will deal with later. But first, and for the moment, foremost, is the issue of ignorance. In this single, simple idea lies the key to your political, economic and social turmoil. As a species, you are programmed to survive by rooting out ignorance. The state of lacking knowledge, being uninformed, makes you uncomfortable. You need reassurance; you have a biological need for patterns of ideas that can bring order to the mysteries of the worlds you encounter. Ideologies, those patterns of ideas that make sense of the world, are your lifeblood and have always been so. I have already given you an account of the industrial revolutions that shape the world you experience. I have pointed out that for most people in the developed world – although not all – the old forms of religious belief in a creator God have become less – shall we say – satisfying. Fewer people now bring sense and order to their worlds of ignorance and uncertainty through the constructs of religious faith. For many, the glitches in the constructs leave them too uncomfortable – resurrection, perhaps at a pinch, but a god of love in a world of pain, suffering and cruelty? A step too far for many.

"Yet your need for protection against the soul-wrenching fears induced by ignorance grows ever more pressing as the sum of your collective ignorance multiplies. Those industrial revolutions over the last quarter of a millennium have been the product of seminal but quite restricted breakthroughs in human understanding. Many humans were – and some still are – engaged in the mass production of goods in factories, but few of them understood the science or the technology that underpinned the industry in which they worked. And we continue to see further advances in knowledge bases such as digital science that relatively fewer and fewer people really comprehend. Do the likes of Head Boy and Pocket Money or No Benefit understand what goes on under the bonnets of the automobiles, or within the cabs of the trains, that provide their transport on land? Or within the control systems of the aircraft that speed them to other destinations? Do they comprehend fully the knowledge base that underpins the digital revolution? And if they do not – with their privileged and exceptional education and life experiences – how many others of the human race actually have much inkling of quite what is going on in their worlds?

"Now of course the easy answer that surfaces straightaway is that we do not need to concern ourselves with these matters. We leave all this to those who do know. The experts. The specialists. Those we trust; those in whom we have faith. Meanwhile, we can get on with what we know we can do. Driving cars and trains, flying planes, tapping messages on computers. Governing countries, running economies, looking after people's needs…"

The Interpreter paused. "Do you begin to catch my intent?"

Pilgrim nodded, thinking hard, and his guide continued.

"The human species finds itself, particularly in the developed world, better educated than it has ever been before, in the sense that universal compulsory schooling is a taken-for-granted fact of life. Yet as a species, humanity has never before experienced such collective ignorance about the world in which they live. As a species you have a built-in capacity to reflect upon how things are in the world, how they have been and how they will be. Other creatures seem not to have been graced with this human facility. Ants live their ant existence; they do not develop paradigms of meaning and purpose. Humans, on the other hand, do. At some level of consciousness, you know there is so much you do not know or understand. You know your own ignorance. That is not a comfortable thought. Since you are programmed to protect yourself, to adapt to the environment around you, most people will bury that sense of ignorance. Sublimation is a reasonably efficient and effective coping mechanism, albeit with variations in shelf life.

"But living in a state of ignorance also produces a hunger for truth that can leave people clinging to false certainties. Ignorance can be denied not only through sublimation, but also by the construction of towers of meaning whose foundations are at best provisional and at worst rotten – that is, devoid of true knowledge.

"These are matters of profound importance, Pilgrim, in considering the nature of democracy in a world which is shaped by market forces. Your quest for truth and understanding, your need to make sense of and alleviate the suffering you find unbearable, requires your grasp of these matters. The human individual as an elector is faced with a choice of competing messages, each party or individual offering their particular prescriptions for good government. It may be that none of these messages actually hits its target. It is possible that the veil of ignorance is so extensive that all these prescriptions are fatally flawed. Democracy as an idea is a cruel hoax. A phantom ideal, spun from good yarn into toxic cloth by the fractured spirit of Mammon for his own ends. There would certainly, as they say, be some mileage in that idea. But the Lady Hope would have a different view, and Charity herself exists to overcome such malevolence.

"Let me now explain how one particular strand in these political messages has come to have such prominence. After your encounters so far on this journey it will be interesting to hear your reactions."

And the Interpreter began to weave an explanation around a putative field of scientific enquiry that had become a desert of make-believe. He turned to the subject of economics.

"Head Boy and Pocket Money and their team of gamesters went into politics with some basic beliefs about society and economics. People were better off paying less taxation. The state was too big, too expensive. The market flourished more successfully for all when it was allowed to be freer, with less regulation. These were the ideas they grew up with as children, communicated by the adults around them, and turned into political credos in their own early adult life.

"At the same time as these gamesters were children, within the universities of the English-speaking world, a remarkable phenomenon occurred. In every department of economics, there was a cull. From the 1970s, all ways of analysing economic problems vanished from the curricula – bar one. And that one surviving theory was called Neoclassical Economics. It had first seen the light of day in the 19th century. Now, for over a generation, economics has become the only academic discipline where issues of the 21st century are examined in the light of a single outdated way of accounting for the relationship between humanity and its money transactions. This theory was always suspect, and now, ever since the banking crisis that threatened the collapse of global capitalism erupted in 2008, it has been proven demonstrably false."

Pilgrim interrupted. "But how could such a thing happen? I think of universities as places of learning, not dictation."

"A fine idea!" replied the Interpreter. "Treasure it. The explanation is rooted in money. In the USA the top eight universities were enticed by military and industrial dollar-power into narrowing the focus of their economic departments to fund research into an economics that reduced matters to the mathematical. The military believed that such research would have important benefits for national defence. Such is the thinking that shapes the human world. And then Power followed Power. Other universities followed suit. Neoclassical economics became enshrined as the definitive economic doctrine. Within a generation, international bodies were staffed and run by graduates shaped by this doctrine." [21]

"So when a gamester like Pocket Money says his policies will restore the nation to prosperity, he has the backing of high learning," cut in Pilgrim.

"That is so. But I am arguing that it is corrupted high learning."

Pilgrim's eyes widened, but he said nothing. The Interpreter continued.

"Let me take you back to the time shortly after you arrived at the election victory arch and entered Vanity Fair. Pocket Money, in his role as government minister, addressed the nation and presented his solution to the problem that had been left after the rescue of the banks a couple of years before. That problem is called the structural deficit. Put most simply, that just means the amount by which government spending exceeds its income. Pocket Money said that the structural deficit was 4.8% of our output as a nation. He said we had to make sure that those we borrowed from in international money markets did not become alarmed and think us a bad risk, and charge us more interest on our loans and so make the situation even worse. He said his government would

42

eliminate most of that deficit in five years. In other words, in the lifetime of his government, which had changed the law, as soon as they were elected, to ensure there would be no election before five years.

"How would this deficit reduction be achieved? Government spending had to be cut. The state was too big for its own good. Pocket Money said that within three years the deficit would be down from nearly 5% to less than 2%. Well, three years later and after nearly £60 billion of spending cuts and tax rises, the deficit was still over 4%. Basically, over halfway through their time in charge of this democratic state, the political gamesters in charge of the country's fortunes had failed in what they claimed was their single biggest economic ambition."

The Interpreter paused. Pilgrim continued to look at him intently, waiting for his guide to continue.

"The reasons why their policies failed are clear enough, and were anticipated by those who opposed the new government. But before we examine those reasons, remember the link between cutting government spending and reducing the size and influence of the state on the one hand, and the health and well-being of the lives of the citizens of that state on the other. The government itself acknowledged that there would be pain ahead, but the gain would make it all worthwhile in the long run. And we were all in this together, they assured the nation. So, Pilgrim, as you make your progress on your journey through the five years allotted to this government on this island, keep a note of the balance sheet account. How much pain has been suffered – and how much gain enjoyed – by how many individuals from how many different walks of life in this nation?

"As to the reasons for failure, some people might say that it was because they made the schoolboy error of thinking that running a country is like running a family household budget. Cut public spending by government and so reduce the hole in the nation's finances. Private enterprise will end up employing those who have lost their public sector jobs. There were times when Pocket Money and the other political gamesters' own words suggested that was their way of thinking, but let's give them the benefit of doubt and assume they were smart enough to know the difference between a family and a state budget. But they still got caught in the politician's trap of assuming that their compulsory and universally educated electorate were too ignorant to understand the subject of economics, and too blind to see the truth that it is not a science like physics or mathematics. Perhaps they are still deceiving themselves on these matters.

"Let's accept that they did understand that there would be a knock-on cost from cutting government spending, such as people losing jobs and being unable to pay taxes on earnings and needing state welfare payments. Economists call this kind of cost the multiplier. Let's say they assumed that for every £1 billion removed from government spending, around half that sum would be lost to the national economy because of the knock-on costs such as lower tax revenues and unavoidable increases in welfare payments. But even allowing for this 50% loss, the nation's still half a billion pounds better off. So it's good bookkeeping and good politics."

Pilgrim frowned. He was following the logic of the argument and did not like the conclusion. The Interpreter saw Pilgrim's reaction and continued with a reassuring glance.

"Do not concern yourself unduly, dear Pilgrim. My interpretation remains that this is a failing government. Let me explain further. Suppose they got the multiplier wrong. Suppose their obsession with political aims meant they deceived themselves and underestimated the effect of this multiplier…"

"Did they? Deceive themselves? Or was it more calculating?"

"A sharp question, Pilgrim. I think you will find the most satisfying answers to difficult questions are those that accommodate as many positions as possible on the spectrum of explanation. Humanity is the most advanced and complex adaptation in species development that we know about so far.

"What we now know for certain is that the new government got their calculations wrong. An international group of economists called the International Monetary Fund – the IMF – which itself has in the past pressed the case for government austerity across the planet, issued a report around halfway through this government's life in which they concluded that every £1 billion removed from government spending in austerity cuts could have removed almost the same again – another £1 billion – from the economic output of the nation. Or even £1.7 billion! Those figures would suggest a serious attempt at digging the grave of one's own economy." [22]

Pilgrim's eyes had widened even further. It was not that he did not understand the Interpreter's journey into economics; rather that he could hardly believe his ears. The Interpreter brought his explanation to its conclusion.

"Your journey is a progress towards understanding, a search for the truth about the ways in which we are best governed and how we are actually ruled. Since the industrial revolutions transformed the nature of our world, all governments face the problem of having responsibility for a dimension of national life – the economic – that has very few certainties and is clouded by error and political and academic ideology. Deception and self-deception seem the order of the day. This government of yours has vowed to protect health and schools from their public spending cuts. They also feel the need to protect that part of the welfare budget – around two-thirds – that goes to pensioners for fear of the electoral consequences: losing the grey vote in the ballot box in the general election. Hospitals, schools and pensions take up the great majority of government spending and are effectively ring-fenced from cuts. [22] But the gamester in the politician knows that the rhetoric of needing to cut is going down well with the voters. Surveys show that people are turning against spending on welfare and wildly overestimating the number of welfare claimants, the amount paid out, and the numbers cheating the system. [23] Austerity as an idea has provided an opportunity for spin and deception. It has been, dear Pilgrim, an occasion for the display of wilful economic ignorance and miscalculation that has touched and ruined so many lives across the planet, and not least here, within your own sight and knowledge in this land."

"But can people be so blinded by their own beliefs that they cannot see the suffering their actions cause?" Pilgrim asked.

"Humans see what they want to see. If there is suffering, there must be an explanation that lays the blame somewhere other than outside your own door. Scapegoats, you will find, are very useful... Genetic stupidity is quite a convenient call;

some are born into a life of poverty and ignorance, lacking the brains to lift themselves from their unequal lot. [24] The people who matter are the people you truly recognise as people. Your people. Others may bear a resemblance but are not truly quite like you and yours. You used to be very fond of a story about a man from Jerusalem who fell among thieves and was beaten and left for dead. His people – the ones you would expect to come to his aid – passed by. The one who stopped and helped was the man from Samaria, the scapegoated one, the tribal outcast; the genetic loser. People who tell stories like that – or spread them around – are bad news for the rich and powerful who define which people are 'in' and which are 'out'. Storytellers like that can have a short shelf life." [25]

Pilgrim nodded in agreement. He looked down to pick up his load, filled with a measure of renewed determination. He swung the load onto his back and found himself alone again, striding along the road he knew was his to follow, heading towards what looked like another tavern, by the roadside, in the distance, at the top of the hill ahead.

PILGRIM ENCOUNTERS ALF PRICE AT THE CRIPPLE'S EASE

The sign outside the inn was like no other that Pilgrim had ever seen. As he got closer, towards the crest of the hill, he could just make sense of the lettering in the bright sunlight, picked out in unlit neon lights in a long, thin display cabinet that ran the upper length of the granite-faced, mock-Palladian exterior of the building, which was itself set back a few feet from the road and surrounded on all sides by a moat crossed by an antique wooden drawbridge that marked the entrance to the inn.

The Cripple's Ease.

Pilgrim stopped on the road outside, opposite the entrance, looking across the lowered drawbridge through the open door into a seemingly empty and silent interior, towards what appeared to be a bar with its backcloth of bottles and glasses. He looked a little nervously from left to right. There was something about this place that seemed not quite as it should be. Not just the building – he was getting used to quirkiness in this age in which he found himself – but in the air around him. A slight whiff of something unhealthy. It was like the lingering odour of decaying rat.

He looked more closely and saw a curtain move in an upstairs room. He heard a door slam upstairs, feet descending a staircase, and then a cry of welcome from the man who now appeared, waving at him, behind the bar. Pilgrim summoned his strength and advanced across the bridge into the bar.

"Good day! Good day! Good day!" The barman's greeting was enthusiastic. The words seemed to tumble out of him. The torrent continued to flow. "We've been expecting you but had no way of knowing exactly when you'd turn up. You know how it is. Word gets around. The Cripple's turn, they said. What can I get you? You're state funded aren't you? You don't have private insurance. Not that it makes any difference when you are a distinguished visitor like yourself. Let's think of you as an associate inspector with the usual privileges. So what will you have? A Patient cocktail? Now that's worth waiting for!"

The barman grinned. Pilgrim glanced at the assortment of liquids and concoctions in the glasses behind the bar, then shook his head. His host was wearing the long green gloves of a surgeon.

"No thank you," said Pilgrim. "I'm not sure your tastes are quite mine. What is this place? It doesn't seem quite real. It's more like a stage set."

"Really? Don't ask me," said the barman. "I'm just the monkey. Now the organ grinder, he's the one you want to interrogate. The barman grinned again and pointed upwards. He indicated the door through which he himself had entered behind the bar. Come on through. I'll take you up to his room. We all know him here as Alfie. Alf Price. Mr Alfie Price!"

He giggled in a fashion that almost triggered a memory for Pilgrim, but the thought was too fleeting. Pilgrim followed the barman round behind the bar, through the door, up the stairs, and found himself outside a closed door, alone, at the top of a darkened staircase. His host had slipped silently away. Pilgrim knocked once, quite loudly, it seemed to him. There was a long pause.

"Enter!"

The voice was mellifluous and commanding. Pilgrim entered.

In a room stripped to its barest essentials, one master-desk and two chairs, there sat, half-concealed behind the massive desk, the same surgically-gloved figure of the barman who had first greeted him at this wayside inn, The Cripple's Ease. Pilgrim's face betrayed his shock.

"Don't concern yourself with our little ruses, my dear Pilgrim…"

Pilgrim felt himself tense. He trusted only the Interpreter to address him like this.

"I understand your sensitivities, my friend, but we like to lighten the tone and change the roles from time to time. Do please indulge us."

The man rose from his chair and extended his gloved hand towards Pilgrim who, somewhat bewildered, shook it.

"Excellent! Pleased to meet you, Pilgrim. My name is Price. Alfred Price, aka Mr Alfie Price. When you reach my exalted position you revert to plain Mister. I'm the man in charge, the democratically elected government appointee. What you are about to hear is my vision for a transformed national service that will ensure this country enjoys the best state health facilities in the civilised world. Our business is health. Remember, the health of the nation is the wealth of the nation! Better still, our health is our wealth!"

Pilgrim heard the giggle again and remembered. It was the same sound as Pocket Money had made at the Free Market Inn.

"So, Mr Pilgrim, what shall we tell you? Yes! The truth, as ever… Where shall we begin? Yes! I know. The market! That's where we'll start. And that's where we'll finish too. You were once so nearly persuaded of the virtues of the market… it was such a shame to see you lose your way. Not that we blame you. Of course we don't. It's those bloodsucking lefties, those chattering empties from Cloud Cuckoo Land who've leeched onto you. They're the ones!"

Price's tight fist swept down towards the desk, froze just before impact, and then landed with a dull thud. Mr Alfred Price was still in control.

"How sad," Price went on, "that you haven't yet been able to see for yourself the fruits of the market and understand their value, even though part of you knows there's never been a time in the history of this island when so many people have enjoyed so much well-being. And why? It's the market, dear boy. It's the market! The more you open up our world to market forces, the more money there is to be made. The more money that's made, the more the world benefits. Everyone's a winner. The brightest and best achievers transform the services and products we all need, and they get their just rewards for doing so. Governments do less and do it better. We all pay less in taxes to the state because we've shrunk the state. The ordinary man in the street is better off, and he's got more efficient services to fall back on if he is in genuine need. What's more, the skivers and scroungers that have been feather-bedded for too long in the name of welfare get their wake-up call, their comeuppance."

Mr Alfred Price looked pleased with himself. Pilgrim hesitated. The man seemed so sure.

"But why should looking after our health be a reason for making lots of money?" Pilgrim asked. "Doctors and surgeons have always charged for their services; chemists for their pills. Fair enough, if they don't overcharge. But why would you want to set up a market stall in medicine deliberately to make more money – out of our illnesses?" Pilgrim was startled at his own words even as he spoke. That's what it boiled down to – making profits out of misfortune, out of people's ill health. He remembered the Interpreter's account of commodification and the penny dropped.

"Exactly!" Alf Price exclaimed. "You've got it. The more you open up services and manufacture to the possibility of doing deals, the more deals you do, the more money changes hands, and the more money is made. Everyone's a winner! People are always going to be ill. It's a fact of life. Every fact of life is a market opportunity if you approach it in a sensible and civilised way. We are making our National Health Service, our NHS, more cost-effective. Look, do you know how much the NHS costs to run each year? Over £100 billion. Two billion pounds a week. That's an awful lot of taxpayers' money. Let's say there are around thirty million income taxpayers in our population of sixty-four million people. That's taking over £3,000 from every income taxpayer in the land every year. I want – we all want – a service we can be proud of, but not one that just eats up more and more of our money. We can make it more efficient by getting rid of the layers of bureaucracy that just soak up the expenses. We're giving control to doctors and nurses who really do know what needs to be done, and we're introducing a sensible degree of competition into the service so the patient gets the best deal at the lowest possible cost." [26]

Pilgrim felt confused, and then sensed the faintest of touches, like the lightness of a feather, falling on his shoulder. The Lady Hope? Mr Alfred Price continued.

"Now, we know that there was a time in the history of this island when we lost control. The people had fought a war and thought it was time to give the lefties their head, let them have a go at this governing business. Well, we were back in power within six years but not before they had done their worst, nationalising first this industry and then that one. Eventually we got rid of all that nonsense, but we've been left with the biggest nationalisation of the lot: the nationalisation of medicine, the state takeover of health. [27] The problem is that until now it's been rather popular. The people seem rather proud of their NHS. [28] And we haven't been too concerned until now because we still have our private health care for those who are prepared to save to pay for it. But now it's different. We have a real crisis in the state."

Mr Alfred Price looked intently at Pilgrim.

"As you have heard, there is a huge budget deficit and we owe that to the incompetence of the last government. We need to control our spending as a nation. We need to kick-start the economy. And what's more, we've hearing more and more stories about the NHS going wrong. [29] People are waking up; they are beginning to lose their innocence, their simple faith and trust. You see, Pilgrim, every crisis is an opportunity to repair the damage done by others. [30] That's why we've had the courage to redesign this monster of the lefties' so the nation still gets its illusion of free health care – at a real cost of nearly £50 a week for every taxpayer – but we make sure that it's private enterprise revitalising the arterial flow in the beast. In time, we'll have a new privatised model NHS that we can proudly claim as our own."

Pilgrim rose from his chair and extended his hand towards the government appointee, Mr Price.

"Thank you for your time. You've given me much to think about. I'm sure we'll meet again."

Pilgrim swept his load onto his back, turned and faced the door and stepped towards the exit. As he did so, he felt the heaviness of the burden lift. His eyes closed in relief. When he opened them again, he was back on the road, The Cripple's Ease out of sight behind him, and the Lady Hope beside him.

THE LADY HOPE REVEALS MORE

"You did well." The Lady Hope's three syllables were like the freshest and most thirst-quenching water sipped, scooped hand to lip, from the purest hillside stream ever dreamt.

"It's never easy to resist the flow of easy words from gamesters like these, who have studied the art of selling a product. But instinctively you've now grasped that you are still your own person. You are not their creature. You – everyone – can still say no to their word-magic. The power to say no, to resist, to blow away their clouds of concealment still lies with – who shall we say? – you and the rest of the mass of humanity."

Pilgrim felt uneasy with the idea that the Lady Hope saw him as somehow representing the mass of humanity. But the thought, nevertheless, couldn't help but please him. The Lady Hope inspired him. At times like these, when her presence took manifest form and the white-gowned figure really was beside him on the road as he journeyed, it was bliss. The world began a new orbit the moment she was inside his mind, but when she was actually next to him every tiny detail turned the right way up and decaying particles of greed and deception began to fall to the floor.

"My Lady, my debt to you is already great, but will you not this time stay with me for a few more days on my journey?"

He remembered how she had parted from him outside the Free Market Inn.

"Dear Pilgrim! Your journey is towards the truth. You want to discover more about what makes the world a better and kinder place. You have a noble purpose. Do not fear my leaving you. I cannot stay any longer than you really need. In these perilous times I have others to administer to across the world, as well as within this island, and I have many, many identities. I will, though, rest with you a little while, long enough to tell you more about the struggles of my gender, the female sex, and my part as Hope."

A memory of a woman and children, a family abandoned, a journey to satisfy his own needs – Pilgrim's mind filled with confusing thoughts when he heard the word 'sex' from the Lady Hope herself. He had been feeling so good, so inspired. Now, he sensed a little discomfort.

"Much has changed since your last pilgrimage, my bold seeker after truth," Hope continued. "You have already learned that women now have the same right to vote as men do. But do you think that deep down, men and women treat each other as equals? After all these millennia of male domination? When for so many generations women were defined by a man's lust for sex and power, alongside his biological and social need for children and family, not to mention his requirements for food and house-keeping. Consider this question: do men hate women?

"Misogyny is an idea for you to dwell on. Hate and fear are closely linked. Do men fear women? Have you ever wanted to dominate a woman, Pilgrim, out of fear or lust? Have you ever treated a woman badly and then deceived yourself that it was not a hate-filled thing you have done?"

Pilgrim looked ahead, his eyes not meeting hers. The Lady Hope rested her hand lightly on his arm.

"Let me tell you this story of how I befriended and became Lizzie. How she became one of those many identities I've assumed since the free market gained the upper hand and austerity became the new order.

"Lizzie had needed me at several points in her life already. She had been born into a decent and caring enough family, but one in which her two brothers were the focus of whatever limited expectations the father and mother had for their family. She gained a modest collection of less-than-significant certificates from her schooling and started work as a shop assistant. Within a year she was pregnant with the child that she and the motor mechanic had conceived in the darkness outside the back of the nightclub. The father she chose never to acknowledge. She had been very drunk at the time. But the child, who she named Tracey, did give her hope. And in those days, before the shadow of austerity came across her horizon, there were schemes for young mothers like her to return to education, with a nursery playgroup place for her child at the local college. Within three years, she had secured the qualifications that reflected her abilities and got a full-time post as a junior civil servant in the local office of a government department.

"But almost immediately there came the banking crash of 2008. For two years, that made little difference to her life. And then came the Election Fair that you already know about. The new government was determined to cut the size of the state in order to reduce its running costs so as to eliminate the debt incurred by bailing out the banks. A lot of money began to be taken in the name of the people to mend a very large hole in the fabric of capitalism. Many of the people employed in the public sector were being made redundant in the name of efficiency. Lizzie lost her job. She stopped being a taxpayer and her economic utility diminished. She became a burden on the state in the eyes of a growing number of people who were being fed a diet of media propaganda that sought to justify the neoliberal ideology of the new government. Lizzie became depressed. She had no choice other than to sign up for employment with an office cleaning firm that offered her only a minimum wage and a zero-hours contract that meant she had no guarantee of regular employment, no holidays, and no sick leave.

"She needed me, and I answered that need. Only the support of her own mother, who would take care of Tracey as and when needed, made the arrangement possible at all, and I made sure that happened. But then came the next blow in the name of austerity. The council flat that she had secured when Tracey was born had been allocated to her in an area that few applicants wanted for their home. But it did have a third bedroom, which Lizzie now used for her mother to sleep over when Lizzie was forced to get up in the middle of the night to work a shift. Out of the blue came the government's new directive. Her home was to be taken away from her and passed on to a family with more children. She was occupying too much space. Six months later, Lizzie and Tracey had been rehoused thirty miles away, severing the immediate link with her mother's support. Her contract with the cleaning firm ended. Her old home remained empty. The larger family in need never materialised.

"Again she needed me, and I am answering that need. Hope is everything. But when I look back and see the grubby pointlessness of her suffering I am moved. I am angry. Not least because all this comes from a government shaped by male brutality and indifference to suffering. I hope, dear Pilgrim, you have the stomach to listen and understand fully. You are carrying the burden of your own gender along with all the suffering that moved you to begin your journey. And they are connected." The Lady Hope looked intently at Pilgrim. He met her gaze and shivered involuntarily. When he spoke, he did so with remorse.

"My understanding deepens, my Lady." The Lady Hope reached out again, and this time her hand held his arm.

"And all shall be well. The Interpreter will continue to help you with his accounting. I will be there whenever you need me. Charity will come when the moment requires. But this journey also requires you to develop. You have to become more skilled in understanding your true human nature. Learning how to feed your soul-spirit as a member of a flawed species. Recognising your own taste for Mammon. You have to understand how to keep a measure of company with those who would use you – for that is unavoidable – and remain untainted. But remember, you are doing well – very well!"

Pilgrim had closed his eyes to avoid the moment of loss. Now he looked around and the sense of being alone hurt. He had few features of the embodied Lady Hope to recall after her appearance. The whiteness of her gown was one, her smile another. The rest was strangely unknowable, as if it had been seen and then dissolved from his memory. But her smile was a solace, the smile of approval. That he could treasure as he moved on down the highway, knowing it would not be long before he had the stimulus of the Interpreter's accounting again.

And his burden was less. The weight he had borne on his back was now gone. He was luggage-free.

PILGRIM DISCOVERS A CRISIS OF THE FIRST ORDER

Pilgrim was no longer surprised by the twists and turns of a road that played fast and loose with time and space. He had come to a halt at a turn in the road that was signposted by a single letter, H, when the Interpreter appeared and beckoned.

"Greetings, Pilgrim. Come! I will explain as we observe."

The next moment, Pilgrim was beside the Interpreter on a viewing balcony overlooking gowned and masked figures standing below them, gathered around a body lying on a table. The scene was suffused with brightness.

"We have become unseen observers of one of the miracles of your modern age," the Interpreter said. "Below us, a team of rigorously trained, highly qualified and experienced surgeons, anaesthetists and nurses are performing triple heart bypass surgery on a forty-five-year-old man, one of your sixty-four million citizens. A postman by occupation, an ordinary man in the street, a citizen without the wealth to pay for such an operation. His treatment is almost certain to be successful, and the man's life expectancy will be lengthened by thirty years. He will live to see his grandchildren born and thrive. They will remember him with love and affection, their lives enriched by his zest and relish for life. The total costs of this one operation and the man's hospital care before and afterwards run to well over £20,000. And he will pay nothing directly towards this. This treatment of his medical condition is his due right. This is your National Health Service. Free at the point of delivery, from cradle to grave; for all, regardless of income, wealth, or status, with medical need the only criterion for treatment."

The Interpreter paused as the operation taking place beneath them reached a point of completion.

"That is the miracle we are celebrating, Pilgrim. In a world defined by industrialisation and the release of global market forces, on a planet where the spirit of Mammon had been licking his lips over a cup that was filled to the brim and spilling over with opportunity, here, in this island of yours nearly seventy years ago, the people of this land, having just played their own vital part in the defeat of a diseased ideology and state, used their democratic mandate to elect a government that had an ideological commitment to what they called socialism. They had an election manifesto that promised to secure for the workers – for the ordinary people, the vast majority of the population – what they said would be the full fruits of their labour. How? This new government would take over what they called the means of production, exchange and distribution. In other words, the state would take over the ownership of roads, rail, steel, docks, coal and public utilities such as gas and electricity from the private individuals who had owned them as shareholders. And they did." [31]

The Interpreter, throughout his explanation, had been following the procedure below as it was performed out by the gowned figures. He now turned his face directly to Pilgrim's.

"It lasted scarcely more than a generation, this spirit that the people of a nation could act together in their common interest to ensure that the world became a fairer place in which to live. Just over thirty years later, a new government, committed to the old values of individualism and private profit, low taxation and high levels of wealth creation, came to power and over time all was undone. Even the party that had won the election and formed the government that had given Mammon such a setback eventually abandoned its commitment to public ownership and nationalisation in order to restore its popularity. [32] And yet..." There was a look that Pilgrim glimpsed for a moment in the Interpreter's features. It could have been one of triumph. "And yet one bold, inspired act of this brave government survives to this day. It is the nationalising of medical care through the establishment of a National Health Service. Before it was set up, you had to pay the doctor the equivalent of a fistful of £5 notes before he would even put his foot over your threshold. All that disappeared. District nurses became part of the care system for elderly parents. People's lives were transformed." [33]

The Interpreter paused. "All that is now under threat. They will deny it, of course. They have made it clear on many occasions that the National Health Service is safe in their hands. But this government has a five-year tenure of office in which to ensure that the NHS is permeated by the magic of the market. You have already heard some of what is intended directly from one of their market men, Mr Alfred Price. There is so much more to come..."

The Interpreter gestured to the scene below.

"There is a logic to unregulated market forces and the kind of thinking that justifies the lack of intervention which points always towards greater inequality. If you make a crisis deep enough, you can end up believing that some ideas should no longer be taken for granted. Why should everyone be entitled to the same medical treatment when some people are clearly more valuable to the economy and society than others? When resources are limited and the crisis is continuing – and you have made it very plain that the crisis is continuing and will continue – rationing will be needed. Operations such as this will become unaffordable for all those in need. You can, of course, always have the operation done under private health arrangements. Only the feckless would not have taken out private health insurance to cover such a future need. So those who are worthy will get their entitlement. The rest won't. That will be the new order of fairness and justice, dear Pilgrim, in some future time."

Pilgrim had listened intently.

"But you've explained that this land is a democracy. Why wouldn't the voice of the people deliver a resounding 'No!' to these injustices, to this rolling back of fairness and equality?"

"It's true," the Interpreter said, "that there is another election scheduled five years down the line from the time your journey first started in earnest at Vanity Fair. The voice of the people will be heard then for sure. The votes in the ballot box will be counted and you would expect the judgement of the majority to be against those who are – on my accounting – governing in the short-term interests of the few. Unfortunately, it is not, I am afraid, as simple as that. Come! We will talk more on this in another place. Remember the miracle we have just witnessed, and the vision of a good society that inspired it. And take care. The fogs of deception will fall around you, as they will the voters with the coming of the next Election Fair."

Pilgrim closed his eyes to fix the memory of the miracle. He felt the Interpreter's touch on his shoulder. He looked around and saw, as he knew he would, that they were now elsewhere. They were alone in a bare tent, seated together on a rush-reed floor.

The Interpreter grasped his arm. "Don't be alarmed. We are quite safe here for the time being. We will not be disturbed. I have brought you to the very edge of the field of the new Election Fair. Construction has just started, but we still have over a year before completion. And you have much more to see and learn. Here I can explain more about the voice of the people." And Pilgrim listened as the Interpreter gave his account of how this aspiration called democracy was working in this land at this time. In my dream, I watched them. I heard the Interpreter's words. Pilgrim's journey was mine too.

"The point, Pilgrim, is always in this enlightened age to be found with a ruler and calculator. Insecure times breed the need for measurement. We must fix our parameters, calculate our bearings, and comprehend the scope and scale of everything. If we fail to ascertain our assets, actual and potential, and those of our rivals, we are sunk. So runs the current mythology, and all myths contain a core of truth. The industrial revolutions that underpin this world of yours are founded, as I have explained, on the predictability of events. The new technologies have all required measurement as their very basis. The need for statistical data is real enough. But that need has spawned a surfeit of wants too. There is a craving for the comfort of statistical justification that only leads to falsehoods. Well over one hundred years ago, a phrase had been coined to capture this truth. *There are three kinds of untruths: lies, damned lies, and statistics.*" [34]

The Interpreter leaned forward, and with his finger drew two shapes on the surface of the mat between them. "Here, in this circle, we have the target. In a state that has earned the title of a democracy, that target is the electorate. In your land, that target comprises around forty-six million adults. They are the men and women who can cast their vote once every five years to have some influence over the way they are governed for the next five years. It is at best a rather limited form of democracy, but it has taken much pain and effort to achieve. Here, in this other circle, we have the forces whose representatives you have begun to encounter on your journey to find truth and understanding. It is highly desirable for these forces –let's call them the agents of Mammon – to enjoy the advantage of an elected government that acts in their interests. That is what came to pass after the last gathering of Vanity Fair in 2010 when your journey began. That is most certainly what did not happen in the 1945 post-war election, when the electorate had a different vision which was fundamentally hostile to the forces in this circle, here. As for the governments they elected before this present one, the issue of whose side they were on is a more complex one to resolve. I think it is a fair comment, however, to suggest that even the governments identified as traditionally hostile to unregulated market forces were beginning to dance more closely with those same agencies." [35]

The Interpreter drew a line between the two circles before them. "This is the line of influence. It has become central to political action in a way that continues to prove highly damaging to the interests of those who oppose Mammon and his agents. Understanding the feelings of the electorate now helps governments shape their messages. It may even change those messages, but not necessarily permanently.

Once elected, there are five more years to influence those in this circle – the electorate – through the repetition of ideas in words and images that reinforce the messages they want to convey. But what's essential is the measurement of public opinion, before, during and after these exercises in manipulation. Surveys, focus groups, historical analyses, psychological studies, control groups – every conceivable means to control the slippery eel of democracy. [36] We will see more and more fruits of this activity now that Vanity Fair is beginning to reassemble in preparation for the next election. Remember, dear Pilgrim: they who would deceive the most resort to the black arts of statistics."

"But why can't the lies just be exposed for what they are?" Pilgrim asked. "Why can't the statistics be examined and their validity questioned?"

"Indeed! Why not? Sometimes they are, but always there are the issues of communication. Exposures and examinations and enquiries take place in a real world where people may never have the opportunity to hear and see the outcomes of such truth-seeking, such righting of falsehoods. What you believe to be true depends in part on who you listen to, what you read, what you see. It also depends on the way you are inclined to see the world in the first place. Let me provide you with some statistical data of my own about the electorate, and you must make your own judgement as to its truth-value."

The Interpreter reached into the folds of his gown and emerged with a small, flat, rectangular screen that he cupped between his hands and began to press. Pilgrim was no longer startled by the unexpected in this contemporary journey, but he had not lost his sense of wonder. He knew the

Interpreter was about to extract something extraordinary from this tool.

"So what do the surveys and opinion polls tell the politicians about the feelings of the electorate in our democracy?" the Interpreter asked. "This one, here, was undertaken three and a half years into your journey, a year and a half before the election when you are due to return to the heart of Vanity Fair again. The researchers wanted to explore the reasons why people were put off voting in an election. Can you imagine that? I have outlined a story that takes you through some 350 years from the last journey you made from this land to this present one, and shown you how, over those years, all men and women over the age of eighteen were able to claim the right to vote in elections, bar the insane and, regrettably, prisoners. [37]

"But large swathes of people are now choosing not to exercise their democratic right to vote. Just look at these statistics. In 2010, at the time of the election when you started your journey, 35% of the UK population did not vote. But that was an improvement on the election before that. In 2005, 39% declined to vote, and in 2001, 41% had failed to vote. What a contrast with the first three post-war elections! In 1945, 1950 and 1951 on average only 20% declined to vote. Even as late as 1964, more than three quarters of the electorate were voting, and turnout was roughly equal across the generations. What happened? As the new millennium approached, sections of the British people began to lose faith with their democracy. Some slight signs of recovery now, perhaps, but this survey suggests that the issue has the potential to become even more serious, since it is the younger people – those under thirty – who are more reluctant to vote. In 2010, 76% of over-sixty-fives were still voting, while only 46% aged eighteen to twenty-four were going to the ballot box. So what is the explanation? Anger about broken promises is the key. According to this survey, anger with politicians who do not keep promises is a much more important explicit reason, overall, than, say, boredom or ignorance about politics. Within the youngest group of voters, the eighteen to twenty-four-year-olds, there is an even divide between anger and boredom as their dominant feeling about politics." [38]

"What promises do people think the politicians are breaking?" Pilgrim asked.

"A good question. Some believe that this present government has never been surpassed in its deception, citing the rift between its pre-election words and its post-election deeds. [39] Some may excuse the U-turns on the grounds that the economic crisis forced the hands of the politicians, but overall there does now seem to be a systemic lack of trust in politicians that has a number of roots. The crisis is deeper than just broken promises. My judgement is that so very many people in this democracy are anxious about their future. This period has been carefully painted as an age of austerity. Few are confident that those with power and wealth, not just the politicians but all those with wealth and power, have the desire or ability to concern themselves overmuch with the interests of anyone else other than their own kind. [40] Oligarchy and plutocracy begin to reveal themselves in their true colours.

"One seminal moment in this story of growing distrust, this alienation of the people from their representatives in Parliament, came in 2003. The United Kingdom's Prime Minister determined that this country should join the United States of America in a war against a Middle Eastern autocrat whom their countries had, in other periods, previously supported and then attacked, only to leave in power. A million people took to the streets in London to protest their opposition to such a bellicose policy. Opinion polls showed a massive majority against war. All to no avail. [41] You stretch the rubber band of belief that democracy is for real only so far before it begins to fray. Another key moment came in 2007. Many MPs had been so taken with the injustice, as they saw it, of the relative smallness of their salaries compared with those of their friends and associates in the establishment that they inflated their income from the expenses they claimed from the public purse.[42] You begin to see, Pilgrim, how much fare cynicism and distrust have had to feed on?"

"I would be eyeless not to see that this is a crisis of the first order for democracy," Pilgrim replied. "But what can the people do?"

"By asking such questions and understanding how we have come to this pass, you are providing your own answer. I think that you may now be understanding the purpose of your journey over these years a little more clearly."

The Interpreter reached forward and passed across to Pilgrim the slim rectangular tool that he had been reading, and which had given him the figures and other information he had been citing.

"You will find this of inestimable use in your journey, particularly as you encounter the agents and listen to their arguments. Do not worry. My hands and mind will guide you in its use, as and when the need arises." The Interpreter leant back and folded his arms. "You'll need some time alone with your new fount of knowledge before your next engagement on the road. I think education should be your first subject for study. Very appropriate."

Pilgrim Has a Lesson in Education

Pilgrim looked around and saw the outline of the tent begin to fade.

"It is almost time for you to meet another of the agents of Mammon," the Interpreter said. "He will complete a triumvirate. You have met No Benefit, whose concern is welfare, and Alf Price, whose labour is health. Now it is time for you to discover their take on education, the third great drain on the spending of the state, as they will see it. You will find yourself soon outside the office of the Headmaster himself. Another man of vision. We know him as Dull Mind. See what you make of him."

As the shapes shifted around him, Pilgrim knew he was entering a dimension beyond his comprehension. He remembered clutching the black tool in his hand. Then the sensations of movement began, interspersed with periods of calm, reading the screen like a book as his fingers pressed the buttons.

It had been, he reflected as he now found himself standing alone on a carpet of red, in one sense no more or no less than the dreamscape of his night-time world of sleep. But this was an awakening with a difference. Standing at the end of a long corridor, he realised that he had been gifted with much information about the subject that had been chosen for him. Education had become his specialist subject. He liked that thought very much.

Pilgrim could see that walls on both sides of the corridor were panelled with pictures: framed photographs of teams of young men, garbed for various sports such as rugby, football, cricket, basketball and tennis, whose lines of serious, unsmiling faces were interrupted at regular intervals by larger photo portraits of the great men who had headed this venerable institution. The plush, red-carpeted corridor led to a single door, a massive oak door that emanated authority. In my dream, as I watched Pilgrim surface from his dreamtime, I felt the fears of my childhood rise as the trappings of adult power clicked into their subconscious place. The engraved copper nameplate told the world that this was where the Headmaster lived.

Pilgrim rang the small illuminated bell beside the nameplate. An unseen panel lit up, revealing the command *Enter* in green. Pilgrim turned the smooth doorknob and entered. He had expected the occupant to be sitting, empowered behind the inevitable desk. But the only person that Pilgrim could see in the panelled room, which was covered with framed photographs of school groups dressed in standard blazers, black-and-white photographs on two walls; colour photographs on the other two, stood quietly by the window that overlooked a sports field.

"Good morning! I'm pleased to meet you. I hope your journey here has not been too uncomfortable. Road or rail, it makes little difference these days, does it?"

If this was the Headmaster, he seemed a lighter and more pleasant man than Pilgrim was expecting. Rather charming, in fact.

"Hello. I am the Headmaster of this venerable institution. My job is to ensure that all the children of this land are given

71

the kind of education that equips them best for their role as citizens of our great nation of ours. Do forgive me, I haven't quite had time to establish your full name yet. My secretary has written *See Pilgrim for interview over coffee in morning.* You are Mr Pilgrim? Your first name is…?"

"I think, Headmaster, you will find it advantageous to check out my identity with your line managers," Pilgrim replied. "It would be rather surprising if a man of your standing had not done so already. Perhaps if you were to consult your files?"

Pilgrim was beginning to enjoy his new assertiveness. After his previous encounters, he was ready for whatever these agents of Mammon might have in store for him. The Headmaster gave him a quizzical look. Pilgrim fleetingly speculated as to why the Interpreter had called him Dull Mind.

"I do apologise, my dear man – it's beginning to come back to me now. You are, how shall we say, simply 'Pilgrim'. And you're doing the rounds of us humble shakers and movers, as part of a fact-finding enquiry. Most interesting. You're trying to discover how to make the world a better place, whilst we are actually engaged in making the world that better place. It's the difference between thinking and acting, so to speak. You speculate; we perform. I'll be delighted to spend a little time widening the parameters of your vision. Do sit down. What do you want to know?"

The Headmaster interrupted himself. "Do excuse me!"

He moved from the window to an array of buttons on the desk in the centre of the room and pressed one. Almost at the same moment, the other door in the room opened and a young girl entered with a tray for the coffee break.

"Allow me to introduce Cheryl, one of our new breed of sixth-formers. We move with the time here, always open to change as times demand. Single-sex education in the main school, mixed in the sixth form. Done wonders for our tally of top university places and makes sound financial sense too, as we move to revenue streaming according to league table placing. Invest in the best and satisfy the rest. That's the way forward."

Cheryl smiled politely and handed out the cups of coffee, offering milk and sugar, and then left bearing her tray without saying a word. The Headmaster sat down behind the desk and continued to explain.

"I am, of course, a market man. I see no reason why the power of the market cannot be utilised to help transform the life chances of thousands of bright young boys and girls who have the ability to succeed but are at present held back by being caged in comprehensive schools where a one-size-fits-all mentality denies the best their due rights. We will begin with new institutions that have a not-for-profit charitable status, but I'm sure that in time the natural logic of the market will mean that investors will see the rewards in measured academic achievement. Not that the problem now is just mediocre schools failing the brightest. It's the whole system. Take the examinations. They've been dumbed down for years. And the subjects taught. Gerrymandered to exclude whole chunks of our national heritage. So I'm making sure that my school here – my ideal school – becomes the model for schools all over the land. I've made sure that my school is a free school. Free of local authority interference and free from the manipulation of the so-called expert advisors who only too often are peddling crypto-Marxist flannel. My school is an academic school, proud to bear the name of 'Academy', where children follow a curriculum that values real knowledge, where the works of our great writers – Chaucer, Shakespeare, Milton, Byron, Keats, Austen, Hardy, Dickens – are studied and revered, where the story of this remarkable island and its history is taught and known so that it may be passed on to future generations." [43]

The Headmaster interrupted himself again, with a chuckle. "There I go again – slightest chance and I'm off! How very rude of me. You must have your own questions to ask. And what of yourself, and your journey so far? What impressions have you formed about my colleagues and our enterprise?"

The Headmaster relaxed and leaned back in his chair, indicating with the slightest of hand movements that Pilgrim was free to proceed.

Pilgrim too knew the utility of politeness. "You all have a great faith in the power of the market as a force for good. You all seem intent on using – how shall I put this? – using the power you hold in your offices of state to bend the way things are to how you think they should be, according to your vision of the good life. Is that about right?"

"I could hardly have put it better myself!" the Headmaster replied.

"But tell me, please: on what authority do you undertake your acts of state?"

"I would have thought that was obvious! I am the man in charge of education, one of the great departments of state. My authority comes from the office of state that I hold."

"And is that authority in any way an expression of the will of the people? Does your authority have any democratic underpinning?"

"Of course!" the Headmaster cried. "There was an election that saw our party returned as the single most successful party in the land in terms of votes cast by the electorate. We were able to form a government in coalition with a smaller party who shared our policies on putting right the economic damage suffered during the previous government's time in office." [44]

"And all the reforms you were telling me about – the changes to the curriculum and to the exams, the new types of schools – how far are these an expression of the will of the people?"

The Headmaster gave Pilgrim another quizzical look. "I'm not sure you quite grasp how our democracy works, Mr Pilgrim. The people have the right, every five years, to vote for a government which then has a popular mandate to rule. The party or parties that form that government will have had manifestos, statements of principles and policies. Electors will have voted for particular parties because the electorate trusts that these parties will carry out those policies as far as they are able in the circumstances in which they find themselves. Electors express a preference for a certain way of doing things in the world of politics."

"And the way you do things in the world of politics, Headmaster: was that anticipated in your party's manifesto?" Pilgrim asked. "Do all your changes have the sanction that they were anticipated and generally approved by significant numbers of the electorate?"

The Headmaster stared at Pilgrim and said nothing.

Pilgrim continued. "My point, Headmaster, is that your actions now seem so unpopular with so many people. I understand that you or any of your colleagues will find themselves opposed by those with a different worldview, such as – if I may use the 'S' word – socialists. The ones who fundamentally oppose your broader policies. But you, Headmaster, seem to have hit the jackpot of disapproval in the ranks of the professionals within the fields of education. I have discovered that teaching unions have been passing votes of no confidence in your policies, including – before you say that's what you've come to expect from unions with a political agenda – the National Association of Head Teachers. I've read there was condemnation at their conference last year of what was seen as a climate of bullying, fear and intimidation that had been intensifying since you took office. [45] What do you have to say about such charges?"

The Headmaster smiled patiently. "Politics is a rough business, Pilgrim. Sticks and stones. Sticks and stones. I will do whatever I have to in order to ensure that the bright kids from ordinary families can prosper in life and get a really top-class education in a first-rate school with first-rate teachers. Look, you know the statistics. Seven per cent of our children are being privately educated at fee-charging public schools and the vast majority of those youngsters are getting a great education. [46] Elite schools for the children of the elite. Great news. Our future leaders, the brightest and the best: they are already being nurtured. My concern is to enable, say, another 15–20% of the youth of our country to join them as our future leaders, our captains of industry and commerce and, dare I say it, politics. I don't want bright children to be held back by difficult roughnecks in unruly classes, and by teachers with low expectations and little learning, discontents with chips on their shoulders. Everything I do has that ultimate aim: a society with genuine social mobility. Imagine that, Pilgrim. There's your ideal!"

Pilgrim considered how best to reply. As he did so, with the Headmaster relaxed, contemplating his vision of the ideal, there came the now-familiar sense of time and space dissolving. Pilgrim breathed deeply and waited.

New Voices and New Visions for Pilgrim

The Interpreter's question was not unexpected, when it came. Pilgrim had found himself back on the dirt road again, the digital box safe and secure in his hands. It was a tool that had already given him such understanding. He wished he had had longer with the Headmaster to question him more fully about the consequences of his ministerial use of power. Then the slight moment of contact, and he was no longer alone. The gowned figure of the Interpreter was beside him, the road ahead of them leading downhill to a small village. Smoke was rising from the chimneys of several cottages and houses.

"So why do you think we know the Headmaster as 'Dull Mind'?" the Interpreter asked.

"The more I've thought about the question," Pilgrim replied, "the more interesting I find the answer that's emerging. It's clear that in an obvious way he is far from dull. He's bright and fully engaged, and so are the others I've met on this journey. But I think there's something missing. It's like there's part of his being – and their being – that hasn't been wired as it needs to be. That's the kind of metaphor you would use these days, isn't it?"

The Interpreter nodded.

"And because it hasn't been wired properly, he and the others can't really see the bad effects of what they are doing.

So it's a dullness that's akin to insensitivity. It comes, I think, from being convinced of their own correctness, their own rightness."

"In the language of today," the Interpreter explained, "it's about lack of empathy for alternative ways of making sense of the world. It's having a one-dimensional view on the world. Of course, the great man himself, Professor Marcuse, would say something to the effect that global market forces were behind such a narrowing of vision.[47] I think he's right."

"Marcuse?"

"Herbert Marcuse. He was an influential critic of global market forces some fifty years ago. He wrote about what he called a totalitarian universe in which every aspect of humanity was effectively moulded into what advanced industrial society needed. What you and I would think of as real needs end up being repressed. Democracy has become an illusion. Only those outside the system have any chance of exposing it. He was hardly an optimist, but he did at least see a thin glimmer of hope.[48] You will need more – which is why the Lady Hope is always with you in some form or other. But make no mistake: Professor Marcuse is worth reading. Since the banking crisis and the most recent experience of global market forces under pressure, the basic thrust of his analysis seems ever more relevant. But he can be difficult. I always find it a pity when good ideas are communicated in less-than-straightforward ways. 'Repressive desublimation' is not at first glance the most lucid explanation for the way in which so much human potential is blunted by the dullness and conformity that the market requires."[49]

"I like things to be as clear as possible, too," Pilgrim agreed. "Let me see if I understand. The Headmaster and the others agents of Mammon are all dull-minded because they have been moulded that way by the very system they are fighting to protect. Their insensitivity is a consequence of their politics. They cannot, of course, see it themselves. But self-deception I already understand, only now I'm seeing the idea from a different angle. A global perspective in which all humanity, as it comes under the influence of the narcotic of materialism and market forces, ends up duller and less fully human. Is that the sum of it?"

The Interpreter smiled with satisfaction. "The Headmaster might be proud of your progress, if it were not so much to his disadvantage. Yes, I think you are certainly on the right track. You were always adept at assimilating the truth, dear Pilgrim, although you were perhaps rather single-minded in your convictions on that last journey of yours, before humanity experienced the mixed blessings that have come with industrialisation. You could, for instance, have shown more empathy towards poor Ignorance. You saw only pitiful self-holiness and a passage to Hell for him. He made no such condemnation of you in the Dream." [50]

Pilgrim looked at him blankly.

"No matter," the Interpreter said. "Forgive me teasing you. I know you have little memory of those times now. But empathy is a vital skill. It holds a prized place in the armoury of weapons you will need to combat the influences of Mammon. Neglect it at your peril. But first, let's establish what is right and what is wrong. Professor Marcuse would have been pleased to see the growing criticism of those economists who are hooked on the idea they call 'utility maximisation' to explain the mystery of life. They assume that all that matters to people is getting the most for themselves out of any situation or deal. How remarkable it is that such a limiting and inadequate account should have formed the basis of an academic discipline for so long. Do you remember my earlier explanation for how this travesty arose?" [51]

Pilgrim nodded. That had been one of his first lessons in the uses and abuses of power and wealth in this modern age. The Interpreter continued.

"Since 2008 and the banking crisis, there has been a chorus of dissent against this way of accounting for human behaviour. There are academics who are now repeating what the great economist, J. M. Keynes, used to say: we need an economics based on our knowledge of human nature and the detailed facts of human experience. [52] Other academics are emphasising that the orthodox assumption that economic growth is both necessary and good becomes more and more problematic. They are beginning to explore what a zero-growth economy might be like. Imagine a world with no moneylenders and no interest payments. [53] But communicating this new way of seeing things will be less easy than exposing the limitations in the old methods. The battle against neoclassical economic orthodoxy within universities will itself be long and hard. [54] And the struggle for the hearts and minds of those outside the universities is also fraught with difficulty. Who will put together a political package that says 'Vote for my party – we promise you less of what you falsely want and more of what you actually need. We promise you the chance of a good life'? That's a tall and brave order!"

"But you believe it is possible?" Pilgrim asked.

"I know that as a species you are programmed to adapt in order to ensure your survival and evolution. Since you only became consciously and explicitly aware of that fact quite recently, around 150 years ago, it seems to me more than possible for the species to take and pass a crash-course in adaptation for survival. [55] If unregulated global capitalism thrives on manipulating the very crises it is bound to create, then let's trust in the thriving of those forces that would otherwise be crushed by it. Self-defence is no offence, dear Pilgrim."

"But how can the minds of the people be opened to all these new ways of seeing things?"

"There is no single answer, no single solution," the Interpreter replied. "No one –*ism*. No one godhead of magical recipes. That is a starting point. There are, though, numerous beacons of light. A hundred thousand people at least, mostly young, took to the streets across the democratic world during 2011 and 2012 in what was called the Occupy movement, protesting against an unjust system. [56] There are individual thinkers, with an academic background, whose minds are focused on the problem, and some of their thoughts will hit the mark and spark the chain reactions we need."

"Who?" Pilgrim asked.

"Two of the most important now are Slavoj Žižek and Roberto Mangabeira Unger. For many of you in the English-speaking world, principally in the USA and the UK, there's an immediate problem in their very names. You find it difficult to even pronounce them because by and large you have avoided any fluency in other languages, because your own language of English is spoken universally. There is more than one downside to an imperialist past to be met in post-imperialist times."

Pilgrim, who knew no other language than his own, nodded and the Interpreter continued.

"First, Žižek. He argues that our ways of seeing the world are unconscious systems of belief – ideologies, he would say – that structure our reality and serve to justify the existing social order. But people can still control their lives and shape events, even as they are being moulded by influences that in one sense are beyond their conscious control, *if* they get an inkling of what is real, *if* they learn what is actually happening. Žižek grew up in Eastern Europe in a country shaped by the ideology of communism. He believes that now, across the world, decisions are made by governments in the grip of another ideology. Global market forces." [57]

Pilgrim nodded again. He was beginning to grasp the connections.

"And the other thinker, Unger, is perhaps even more illuminating. Unger criticises Žižek for his lack of a clear vision of alternative ways of structuring the real world, and provides specifics as to how we can change a world that is always there to be remade and reimagined. Matters are never set in stone. Human potential is there to be realised, and we can emerge 'more god-like'. The idea that we are compelled by forces that we necessarily follow is false. [58] Unger actually served for two years as a government minister in Brazil, one of the most advanced developing countries in South America. [59] He's a thinker who is worth knowing about for anyone on the path to greater understanding."

Pilgrim paused to tap and store their names in his black digital box. He and the Interpreter were now directly above the village that lay on the floor of the valley a mile or so away along the winding road. The smoke continued to rise. Pilgrim had a question for the Interpreter.

"Make no mistake, I am understanding more and more how global market forces, capitalism, the ideologies of the political elite – call it what you will – how they work. They have the power to determine the way people think about the world. I remember how close I came to being taken in when I encountered Mammon in person at the last Vanity Fair. And I also know now that there are others who are not taken in by this power, people who stand in opposition to these forces. There is an alternative way of seeing the world. But why has the political opposition been so quiet in this land since the election that marked the start of my journey?"

"That, Pilgrim, is a burning question," the Interpreter replied. "There were some who saw the ideological direction of the new government and imagined a future of concerted opposition, in Parliament and outside, on the streets of the cities. Yet there has been little backlash outside Parliament. The Occupy movement I have already told you about. [60] In 2011, the streets of several cities and towns were in flames as a result of urban riots. But they were hardly straightforward political protests against the government, more spontaneous explosions of mayhem ignited by a cocktail of anger. Fury directed at racist policing by those who felt targeted, mixed with a lust for consumer materialism. [61] The looting from the burning shops spoke volumes about the overwhelming reach of Mammon's power. As for the official parliamentary opposition at Westminster, they are open to a charge of saying and doing too little to explain what has been happening. [62] Is it beyond the understanding of people? Of course not! Will it be ridiculed and twisted and manipulated by sections of the media that are hostile to the opposition? Of course! Does that mean what needs to be said and explained should be left unsaid and unexplained?"

The Interpreter's expression was fierce, as he paused to control himself.

"The official opposition at Westminster elected a new leader after their defeat in 2010, and there have been acts of real political opposition from him on a few occasions. But the overwhelming impression that I get is of an opposition in thrall to political calculation. [63] This is an opposition that says, 'What do we need to do to get the maximum number of votes in the greatest number of key marginal constituencies where our experts tell us the next election will be won or lost?' If that is the measure of what can safely be said in and about the world of politics, if it has come down to a calculation as narrow as that, then we are in real trouble. A politics without a vision to challenge Mammon is not worth the name. It will get short shrift. It will perish."

THE INTERPRETER ON HOUSING AND THE NEEDS OF THE YOUNG

The Interpreter swept his arms out, his outstretched hands indicating the settlement below, and continued.

"Government – democratic government – is done not just in the name of the people, but it is a duty undertaken in the interests of the people. All of them. Not just those below us in that village, but every citizen of the state. Let me tell you what that might mean, and how this present government is failing in its duty. First, let's take the citizen's right to a roof over their head, the housing issue. The manifesto of the Labour party in the 1945 election promised a housing programme to ensure that every family had a good standard of accommodation. [64] The country was emerging from its bomb shelters; the land was riddled with the ruins of homes razed to the ground. In these circumstances, there seemed to be a collective will to ensure that there really was a home for everyone. National governments, both Labour and Conservative, over the next quarter-century, ensured that local authorities built council houses for people to rent. There was a public housing stock to match the privately built houses that were acquired by people who could afford to buy outright, or over time through taking out a mortgage on the property. By 1970, house-building, both private and public, had continued to the point where there was a home for everyone. And throughout this time, house prices remained stable and low."

"That sounds so good," Pilgrim remarked. "Decent and sane government. What happened?"

"Commodification, in a word. What happened is a prime illustration of the power of Mammon. Politicians on both the left and right were looking for policies to win them votes. By the 1970s, many families had become settled in their homes on the new council estates. The idea that they might be able to buy their council estate home at a huge discount and own their property rather than rent it appealed to some tenants. The Right to Buy policy was enacted by Margaret Thatcher's Conservative government after their victory in 1979. Labour embraced the policy in opposition in 1985. A nation's housing stock began to be sold off and, astonishingly, local authorities were not allowed to spend the money they made from sales on building new homes."

"But what did the people who would have rented council property before do now that there were fewer and fewer council houses available to rent?" Pilgrim asked.

"They rented from private landlords, who increased in number as they saw the market opportunity," the Interpreter explained. "A roof over your head had become the subject of commodification and market forces. What was more, the government allowed the original buyers of the former council home to keep the profit when they sold their properties at a market price. Rents rose because the demand rose, with councils unable to build more homes. Higher rents that were proving unaffordable to ordinary people led to massive increases in housing benefit payments by governments that were desperately trying to plug the hole in a dysfunctional market edifice. Those housing benefits – paid for by the taxpayer – ended up in the pockets of the private landlords. And whilst all this was happening in the rental market, house prices took off in the private housing market as demand chased an inadequate supply. Private house-building in this land is controlled by a small group of powerful companies who have hoarded the land they could use for building new homes, but choose not to in order to keep prices as high as possible. We now have a housing crisis of the first order." [65]

"So what can be done?"

"Believe that the problem is soluble, and intervene in the market in the interests of the mass of people, especially the young who face an unprecedented future of high rents and low chances of home ownership. Spend more billions on housing and spend less, say, on transport – someone has suggested that. [66] Introduce a social housing levy on every housing transaction made by the wealthy. There really isn't a problem in coming up with solutions once you accept that in a land that prizes fairness and decency, redistribution of wealth is a necessary social obligation. In such a land, all citizens grow up learning and accepting, in families and at school, that there are certain basic rights that need to be protected against the menace of an unregulated market and its vested interests."

"But getting that kind of acceptance means weaning people off their attachment to wealth," Pilgrim said.

"Exactly. And this is where, in a democratic land, empathy should have more of a part to play. I'll return to that matter when we are nearer still."

The Interpreter swept his hand again towards the village beneath them. Pilgrim had become absorbed in the conversation and forgotten the sight of smoke rising below. The Interpreter continued.

"Before I deal with empathy, Pilgrim – empathy as a weapon of war, mark you – I want to add a further duty to the list that a truly democratic government would wish to follow. I have spoken of the duty to ensure that all citizens have the housing they need, and do you remember I singled out the special unfairness of the exclusion of the young? And there is my further duty. Any democratic government worth its name must govern in a way that takes into full account the needs of the next generation. Government is not just for the present. It must be done with an eye to the future. That is the core message of those who care about the planet and its damaged ecology. Again, do you remember when we first met and I explained the big picture to you, and spoke of global warming? [67] The generation that has claimed the authority to govern in the name and interests of the people has an obligation to govern in the interests of the generations that follow them, their children and their children's children and so on. But market forces and personal interest, the greed of Mammon: all these conspire to blind those in power. The sense of a big picture that embraces the young and their present and future needs becomes distorted. The young who matter to the rich and powerful are reduced to their own children and a feather-bedded future that ignores any bigger picture."

"I want to know more," Pilgrim said. "Give me other examples of how the young have been neglected."

"More than neglected," the Interpreter replied. "They are used. It really is quite shameful, and cuts across party affiliations and labels of left and right. But again, at the heart of the abuse lies the dynamic of an inadequately regulated market, coupled with touches of rather disturbing political incompetence, and what seems at times to be an endemic failure of politicians to see beyond their own electoral considerations. Let me explain. Once more, we need to return to the second great war of the last century. In this land, as people prepared for peace and a successful outcome as victors, the minds of politicians turned to education. They came up with a blueprint for secondary education they believed would provide a suitable compulsory education for all children up to the age of fifteen, according to their talents and abilities. It depended on a threefold division of state schools. Grammar schools for the top 15% or so: the academic elite. Technical schools for around another 15%: those especially skilled mechanically. And secondary modern schools to teach the basic skills to the mass of the next generation. [68] You may remember hearing the Headmaster, when you met him, expressing a view that he wanted his state schools to provide an extra top-up of bright, academically qualified youngsters to join the elite from the public schools. I am sure he had that 1940s model in his mind at the time. [69] What do these plans have in common? A shared belief that people can be divided into those who are born bright and those who are born dull. And those who are born bright seem to be delivered into the homes of the rich and powerful, and those who are born dull usually end up in the homes of the poor and powerless. There are always exceptions, and they must be catered for and absorbed into the ranks of the privileged. It would be foolhardy, a recipe for – what do we say these days? – for terrorism, to leave such brightness, such questioning minds in the ranks of those who experience the downsides to inequality."

"And you don't believe that people are born with different degrees of brightness and dullness?" Pilgrim was considering his own views on the matter even as he asked the question.

"Indeed, I do not. The human species has evolved from other higher primates and possesses an electro-chemical powerhouse – the brain – that is species-specific. There may be glitches and twists in the hardwiring of that brain that become evident in specific individuals from conception or from birth, but by and large human beings are gifted similar human features. You and I have eyes to see, legs and arms to move, noses to smell, lungs to breathe, ears to hear, and brains to use to coordinate movement and thought and language and action.

"The differentiation in the wiring of the brain, the degree of complexity in the arrangement of the axons and dendrites, the whole cellular structure that is opened up by the knife of the brain surgeon, all that is the fruit of the interrelationship between the brain of the individual and the life experiences of that same individual. Here in this land they called it the nature-nurture issue, and debated how much importance should be given to each in explaining our actions in life. Not before time, there are now academic voices pointing out that the so-called debate was asking the wrong question, assuming that nature and nurture could be separated in that way. [70] Why do some people want to believe that there are those who are born dull and others who are born bright? The answer to that question is in the box marked *Power and Control*. Why were women marked out as different from men? Why were they seen as less suited and therefore less capable of fulfilling the political and social roles that men played? Because men feared their competition. Why were those men and women of different races and different colours marked out as inferior by those who conquered and then exploited them? Because power and wealth corrupt. The demand for equality will always be resisted by those whose power and control rest on a foundation of inequality. Imagine: in every state in our world, every member of the next generation is actually born equal, with the potential to enjoy the joy of being fully human. That's such a subversive idea to take on board! No wonder the wealthy and powerful strive to protect their vested interests by denying full human potential to most of the next generation, on the grounds they have been born too dull and lack the brightness to deserve the education deemed appropriate for their own children."

"But that's not what the Headmaster was telling me," Pilgrim said. "He wanted a transformation of the education world so all children could enjoy the best education."

"Listen more closely, and follow the logic of his argument," the Interpreter replied. "His overriding concern is with the youngsters within the state system who have been identified as bright. It is their supposed interests that shape his policies. His world is two-toned: bright and dull. By definition, the dull don't need much education. They require socialisation and training. It is hard to remember now that a great ideal in state education had been thought through and put into practice across most of the land by the 1970s. It was an ideal shared by nearly all, left and right. It was a belief that every young person should be taught according to his abilities and needs in the same school, without the prior labelling of bright or dull. It came from an evidenced-based conviction that the expectations of adult figures – be they teachers, parents, employers or politicians – play a critical role in shaping the thoughts and actions of children. [71] Label a child as dull, and they will give you dull. Label a child as bright, and the light shines forth. This ideal was called the comprehensive school. [72]

"It promised an end to so much wasted potential in future generations. Did you once hear your Headmaster use this 'C' word? No – in the mayhem of new academy schools and new free schools, the comprehensive ideal fades from public view. It is death by omission. Why? Has the comprehensive ideal been tried and found horribly wanting? No. Is there any long-term evidence of systematic failure in the comprehensive school system? No. On the contrary, the comprehensive school experiment has coincided with one of the most significant pressure points a modern society has ever experienced: a radical transformation in many children's experience of parenting. In 1969 in the UK, a Divorce Act was passed that allowed couples to divorce after they had been separated for two years, or after five years if only one of them wanted a divorce. Within a decade, between a third and a half of all marriages were ending in divorce. Imagine the effect on the children of couples deciding to separate in this new world. Imagine the inner tensions brought into classrooms across the land. [73] And yet the teachers still, in overwhelming numbers, continued to succeed in providing the educational opportunities that very many children succeeded in taking. All this, achieved in the face of constant politically motivated attacks on the quality and integrity of the half a million educators in the schools of this land. And now, the present onslaught."

The Interpreter looked away. Pilgrim was silent too. For some seconds there was no movement from either of them. Then Pilgrim spoke.

"I understand the power of the comprehensive ideal. But if expectations do shape performance, wouldn't you expect children in schools to be doing better and better, getting more qualifications for instance? And wouldn't that threaten those who have a vested interest in believing that few are born bright and most are born dull?"

"You would, on both counts. Certainly, there were plenty of influential voices to be heard in the last half-century claiming that our schools were not good enough. They were failing our youngsters, failing to serve the needs of the economy, failing to match the performance of our international rivals. Were those voices really interested in our children for their own sakes? Or was there a political agenda, conscious or unconscious, behind the noise? Were those voices at all aware of what was needed to nurture the comprehensive experiment, and how radically difficult it would be to transform the expectations of parents about the performance of their own children in schools? [74]

"Pilgrim, the educational world has been chaotic and muddled at the best of times in the last half-century, but remarkably, the fact is that ever-increasing numbers of students *did* gain the required qualifications. Clear evidence of success within the comprehensive experiment. And what's more, a political consensus arose to get half of all students into higher education. Universities, which had been the academic finishing schools for the elite, for the top 10–15% between the ages of eighteen and twenty-one, now began to increase in number to meet the new demand for a place at 'uni'. But this was education policy drafted on the back of a postage stamp. Who would pay for all those 'uni' experiences, leading to all those degrees that had been defined as crucial for the future economic prosperity of the nation? [75] It didn't take long before the buck was passed back to the consumer – the student. The university experience had become commodified. [76] The student now borrowed the cost of his or her higher education from the state with the knowledge the repayment would cost, at present, around £26,000 of future earnings, if and when that employment and those earnings materialised. [77] Never mind the rising cost of living in general. Never mind the rising cost of rent. Never mind the rising cost of saving for the deposit to secure the ever more expensive mortgage on the house that you aspire to own. Mind first about the cost of repaying the money spent on getting the degree that your own parents and grandparents would have got for free if they had had your qualifications. Is that a way to nurture the young?"

Pilgrim felt surer than ever of his own understanding of the drama that was unfolding. He spoke with conviction.

"It seems to me, as I listen to you explaining the story, it's like a crime: a crime against humanity that has been running on and on for so long. There has been this long history of denial. The denial of the full humanity of the female and the racially different; and now nearly all the young people who are not the children of the rich and powerful, the so-called bright people. It's awesome in its scale. When I started this journey, I yearned to uncover the true causes of the suffering and distress I saw in the world, and which burdened me more and more. Now my eyes are opening. And in that, too, there is a burden…"

Pilgrim paused. The Interpreter looked at him intently and spoke gently.

"That, Pilgrim, is the burden of responsibility. You must at some point decide not only whether you believe my words, but also what you must do to make sense of your life in such a state of affairs."

The Interpreter seemed for a moment as if he were about to say more, but instead he looked ahead and pointed once more to the village below. "It's now time to consider the issue of empathy as a weapon of war. I fear I may have tested the power of the tolerance you will need too far by these excursions into the uses and abuses of education; perhaps even my own power to empathise, too. We need to rest before I explain more about this village below."

Pilgrim Finds Out Some Remarkable Facts

Pilgrim awoke from his sleep. It was still daylight and he could now smell the wood smoke rising from the village below. The Interpreter was already preparing to resume their journey.

"Come, Pilgrim, we will assume a measure of disguise for this part of your journey. Do not concern yourself. I will take care of everything. The Roma gypsy look, I think – and handmade jewellery. That should do the trick!"

A short while later, the gentle murmur of conversation flowing between the assorted adults gathered together in the front room, and spilling onto the immaculate lawns of one of the large houses that spread along the village riverbank, was interrupted by the cry of a child.

"Mummy! Daddy! We've got strangers in the village. Gypsies!" [78]

The adult conversation froze.

"Call security!" The command was spoken by a man whom Pilgrim would have recognised from a previous encounter in his journey. Seamlessly, from within the house they had been observing and from other houses nearby, a cluster of men and women emerged in twos and threes, all dressed in the same military-style uniform, some armed. Within seconds the remarkable progress of two Roma gypsies into the private village retreat of the great and powerful of the land, and through the mysteriously unlocked garden gate to the point where the trees of the orchard provided some concealment on the very edge of the garden lawn, had been interrupted.

As Pilgrim saw the security forces closing in towards them, he glanced across at his companion. The Interpreter smiled back and whispered, "Time for some evasive action!" The Interpreter touched his arm and Pilgrim knew that he was being lifted out of the clutches of the village. The now-familiar sense of time and place shifting eventually gave way to the warm and secure knowledge that he was back in one of the safe houses of the Interpreter, his guide still beside him. The Interpreter spoke. He seemed a little amused.

"There will be reviews, of course. Who saw what and when? Which command structure was operational in those circumstances, at that time, on that day and on that occasion? In the end, it will be recorded as unresolved, put down to smoke and mirrors with no one certain who was confusing whom, and for what operational reasons. A little seed of insecurity sown. A small shard of paranoia to irritate the garden guests. Nothing too malicious. Besides, the collective defence mechanisms of the great and the good, the rich and the powerful, are pretty resilient. Odd things may happen but do they fundamentally matter? Do they threaten the universe as the oligarchs and plutocrats have shaped it? The default position of the self-deceiver is always to answer: 'No'. Does the flow of data indicating the reality of climate change as a consequence of global warming really pose a threat to the idea of constant growth in the world economy? No. Do the ever-increasing number of stories about the hardships suffered by growing numbers in this land and others, all as a direct result of deliberate government policy and action, mean that ministers should hang their heads in shame and be forced to resign? No. One conclusion, my dear Pilgrim, to be taken to heart above all others – the art of politics starts, for many, with self-deception and leads to the deception of others. And what sustains this sad state of affairs? The idea that all will be well, that all things are for the greater good of all. It's such a democratic notion."

The interpreter was no longer sounding amused. He looked away for a moment and then turned back to Pilgrim, who was sitting opposite him. The Interpreter was focusing hard on the task he had set himself.

"To business. You need explanations to account for our encounter in the village, and you also need to hear my account of empathy as a weapon of war. The two matters are linked, I promise you. First, the village. Despite the necessary singularity of our own lives, my dear Pilgrim, it is as natural as running water for people to seek the company of their own kind. Our excursion to the village was meant as a prelude to my tale of what actually happens on this island, during your journey, when the rich and powerful gather together to enjoy themselves. Our encounter with the security forces serves as a reminder that being wealthy and powerful will invariably lead to a measure of isolation and distance from other worlds. Every world is real to its inhabitants. It's just that some worlds are more cocooned than others. Self-deception is more likely on the planets of Head Boy and Pocket Money. First, let's start accessing our data machine. Press these buttons here."

Pilgrim followed the instruction. The Interpreter continued.

"You see how wealthy and well-established within the so-called elite so many members of this present government are. Press here and see how so many enjoyed similar privileged public school educations. When you're ready, I'll show you how the lives of such powerful people remain interconnected, and further link up with the lives of other powerful figures and institutions. There should be no surprises here, but you will unearth facts and figures that most people either do not know or only half-remember in a sea of data overload. Considerable effort and care is taken to minimise the public impact of such data. I'm sure that by now you will be unsurprised that media manipulation is the order of the day."

For the next couple of hours, Pilgrim's quest for truth continued, his eyes focused on the screen in front of him, his fingers tapping as needed. For a while, the Interpreter sat opposite, saying nothing. Then he began to move around the room, occasionally responding to a question from Pilgrim, who was now intent on arriving at a full understanding of what was happening to the practice of politics in this land. Finally, Pilgrim shut down the digital box and leant back in his chair. The Interpreter returned to his seat and spoke first. "And what have you learned?"

"Many things," Pilgrim replied. "First and perhaps foremost, I learned that the Prime Minister's first and only work outside politics was as a media executive, a professional spinner. [79] And goodness, what a story there has been for any public relations agency to play with! How much ingenuity and skill must have been needed to keep this government on track and still commanding some measure of popular support! When you hold this unfolding tale up to the light and read it through the filters I'm now more and more inclined to use, what a tale of two worlds emerges. On the one hand, there's the collective wealth of a government cabinet packed with millionaires. [80] They are clearly part of the 1%, or 0.1%, whichever figure you choose. They are, through their wealth and personal conviction and public power, helping drive this global inequality and using the mask of democracy to further their own wants. And on the other hand, there is a growing number – a few million, perhaps – of individuals and families, citizens of this land, ever harder-pressed to make ends meet as a direct result of the policies of this government. These cabinet ministers have dedicated themselves to a programme of austerity that has led to cuts in public spending and cuts in the size of the state. All, they claim, to rescue the finances of the country from an economic crash that is presented as the fault of the previous government, and not as a consequence of the actions of a banking industry allowed to run rampant. The deception is breath-taking; the self-deception mind-blowing."

"So far, so very good," said the Interpreter. "And what else?"

"I have learned how the rich and powerful are social creatures and will, unsurprisingly, seek the company of those they can identify as 'people like us'. 'Our kind of person.' People they may fear, people they may respect, people they may use, people they may trust: there are no hard and fast rules, only a shared understanding that they are all on the same side of the fence; that they really are the people who are all in this together. I found the data relating to the so-called 'Chipping Norton Set' riveting, and so revealing. I knew that the Prime Minister of this government was educated at one of the most expensive and prestigious public schools in the country. It's called Eton. But you know that. Anyway, there's a place in this digital box called Wikipedia, the free encyclopaedia, and this really is democratic because it opens up everything to everybody." [81]

"Not quite everything," the Interpreter interrupted, with a wry expression.

"No, of course not – what I meant was that I learnt a great deal from it very quickly about the social worlds of these rich and powerful people. Yes, the Prime Minister went to Eton where the fees alone cost around £30,000 a year, but I also discovered that his father was a stockbroker who also went to Eton, and that the family line goes back through some four generations of wealth creation in the worlds of finance and commerce. Cameron's family is a classic example of an elite family. His mother is the daughter of a baronet and on his mother's side he can trace his bloodline descent back to royalty, to the offspring of a liaison between King William IV and a mistress. Do you know that in his first shadow cabinet, eighteen of its members had been to school at Eton? It's difficult to believe that this old-boy network is so extensive and powerful in a land that has achieved the status of a liberal democracy by wresting privilege and power away from just such forces.

"I know that Cameron has said that you should judge a person on their actions now and not on their background. People should not be criticised and condemned just because they have had a privileged education and enjoy family wealth. Quite so. But it is precisely their actions now that are shaping my judgement. And it is certainly appropriate to make connections between the background of a politician, the friends and connections he enjoys, and the politics and policies he follows – and to draw one's own conclusions. When the historians come to write their account of this land at this time, they will be drawn to the fact that three former members of the Bullingdon Club at the University of Oxford, an undergraduate dining club with a reputation for hooliganism and arrogant bullying, who have been pictured together in coats and tails in a photograph that has been removed from circulation on grounds of personal copyright,[82] are now the Prime Minister, the Chancellor of the Exchequer and the Mayor of London. That fact will serve historians well. That fact will provide a solid basis for a lucid analysis."

The Interpreter nodded and spoke approvingly. "You have used the digital box to good effect, Pilgrim. But there are yet more riches, are there not?"

Pilgrim's eyes widened in anticipation. "Indeed there are! The Prime Minister had a friend at Eton a couple of years older than him called Charlie – Charlie Brooks. Now, I remember that in one of the earliest lessons you gave me as my guide, you spoke of 'political gamesters of the postmodernist kind'. You gifted me a glimpse into the world of Postmutin.[83] That insight has served me well. It shone a light on the idea that self-deception can be assimilated into knowing manipulation. There are those in the ranks of the powerful who take a delight in playing the game of life for all it's worth, in whatever form it comes. That form is to some extent in their own hands since they have the wealth and influence to control much of their experience – but not all, as they know full well. For Cameron, Osborne and Johnson, politics provides the playground for their postmodernist games. For Charlie Brooks, it seems to have been horse racing. He left

Eton to become an amateur jockey and racehorse trainer, and enjoyed some measure of success. His friendship with David Cameron was reinforced when they found themselves neighbours in Oxfordshire, and key members of what's called the Chipping Norton Set, after their nearest market town. David and his wife became close friends with Charlie and his wife, Rebekah."

Pilgrim paused and glanced at the Interpreter, then continued. "At this point, my discoveries became extraordinary. But you know all this already, of course. And more. You know what I don't yet know, don't you?"

"It's true I know already what you have discovered and more still, but I do not have knowledge of the future," said the Interpreter. "I do not have the power to transcend this time-space continuum, although I can act within it in ways that you cannot. The future unfolds as much for me as it does for you. It remains, by definition, unknown in this present time. But you are right. Your discoveries do have something of the extraordinary about them, and as an interpreter of the present and past I would be most surprised if the historians of the future did not find in them much fertile material in their quest to make sense of this period in the story of this island. So tell me what you've found."

"Rebekah, the wife of Charlie Brooks, is not a woman born into the elite," Pilgrim explained. "From humble origins, she had made a career for herself in journalism, with extraordinary success. By the age of thirty-two, in the year 2000, she became the youngest editor of a British national newspaper, the *News of the World*. This was a sensationalist and very popular tabloid within the media empire of News International, an institution owned by one of the most powerful press figures on the planet, a man called Rupert Murdoch. She remained there for three years before becoming the editor of *The Sun*, another hugely popular and influential tabloid owned by Murdoch, for six years. She was then appointed as the chief executive officer of News International. In that same year, 2009, she married Charlie Brooks.

"So we now have this remarkable line-up. First, one of the most powerful press barons in the land, who has access to the Prime Minister in 10 Downing Street whenever he wants, who has cast a spell of respect that seems to border on fear across the world of Westminster politics, who seems to be capable of bending the will of politicians to his own commercial advantage. Then we have his megastar editor, Rebekah Brooks, and her new husband, the Prime Minister's long-term friend from Eton, Charlie Brooks, neighbours and friends to that same Prime Minister and part of the Chipping Norton Set. And there is yet one more face in this line-up: Andy Coulson. A man who was also a newspaper editor in the Murdoch media empire, and the intimate partner of Rebekah Brooks in an affair during her first marriage to an actor in the early 1990s. The Prime Minister made Andy Coulson his Head of Communications in 2012. Murdoch; Brooks, Rebekah; Brooks, Charlie; Coulson – four interconnected players in the world of the rich and famous and powerful. All with connections to the Prime Minister, David Cameron. And then came the phone-hacking scandal."

Pilgrim paused again, his face slightly flushed.

"I could hardly believe this part of the story was for real. In 2012, Murdoch closed down his successful tabloid, the *News of the World*, because of its involvement in the illegal practice of phone-hacking, which had just been exposed. He was reduced to a humble apology before a parliamentary committee. Rebekah and Charlie Brooks and Andy Coulson are now on trial, facing criminal charges related to phone-hacking and perverting the course of justice. I don't know what the outcome will be, but I do believe that these are not matters with which a Prime Minister in a healthy liberal democracy should be associated. You should be judged by the company you keep. Your friends and associates *do* tell a story about the kind of person you really are. I think Mr Cameron must be spinning very hard for more of this mucky business not to be sticking to him."

"I find your line of reasoning persuasive, dear Pilgrim," the Interpreter said. "You have the simple and natural reactions of someone discovering much of the whole story so far for the first time. It is difficult not to be shocked. Do you know, it occurs to me that I have not yet shared Acton's Dictum with you. This you will appreciate. He was a historian who lived over a century ago, and reflecting on his study of past events he observed, *Power corrupts, and absolute power corrupts absolutely*." [84]

"Yes!" cried Pilgrim. "That rings true. We need a democracy as a safeguard against absolute power, but then we also need constant scrutiny of the so-called democrats to protect them from themselves, because power, even democratic power, brings temptation and the potential for corruption. Some so-called democrats will be sheep in wolves' clothing, using the disguise of democracy for their own elitist ends to maintain their wealth and power and privileges; the political gamesters who are in the world of politics for their own personal ends. What perils we face!"

"Indeed. However, do not despair. If the Lady Hope was here in person – and as yet her full presence is not necessary – she would, I am sure, enjoy sharing the wisdom of a man who successfully led the country during its last war against tangible and actual evil, a Conservative who was roundly defeated by the Labour party led by Clement Attlee in 1945: a man called Winston Churchill. Like Acton, he was also a historian and he observed, if I remember right, that no one pretends that democracy is perfect or all-wise. Indeed, he went on, it has been said that it is the worst form of government. This, by the way, was an allusion to the views of the Greek philosopher, Plato, who had a singularly elitist view on life. But then Churchill concluded by saying that it was the worst form except for all the other forms of government that had been tried from time to time. In other words, my dear Pilgrim, we need to make this hard-won way of doing politics work because we haven't found any better way of running a society." [85]

Pilgrim rested his hand on the Interpreter's arm and replied. "You know already that part of my progress, my quest for truth, is complete. I am convinced of the virtue of democracy and I have more understanding than ever of the dangers it faces. I appreciate the thoughts of Acton and Churchill. They are fine embellishments to the map that is now guiding me on this journey. Have you more insights like theirs?"

"Just one for now. Not a historian, but a modern philosopher called John Rawls, an American. He grappled with the issue of what is the just state, and how that just state could be set up in a way that benefitted the people in that state, with all their different interests. His conclusions are valuable. [86] The shame is that their implications are not more widely known and discussed. Rawls offered a defence of the liberal and democratic state that rests on an uncompromising assumption that truth and justice are the prime virtues of social institutions. So you and I can call ourselves genuine liberal democrats, since we hold truth and justice close in our hearts and heads too. Those who don't, can't. So far, so good?"

Pilgrim nodded. The Interpreter continued.

"Rawls also believed in the value of the autonomy of the individual. By this he meant that all human beings are meant to have the best possible opportunity to find the fullest possible expression of their true and authentic nature as a free and equal rational being. You sense the drift of the argument. But that leaves Rawls with the problem of how to visualise a state in which that kind of equality of opportunity can flourish. His solution is a vision of a liberal state in which the individual is guaranteed the protection of his inalienable rights as an autonomous being, at the same time as the major social institutions are so ordered that fairness in the distribution of goods is also assured. The needs of the least advantaged trump all in a society where justice is determined by fairness."

The Interpreter frowned. "The problem, my dear Pilgrim, is that John Rawls, for all his enlightened values and intellectual precision and fine argument, missed the critical point. He was too good an American. He believed too innocently in the dream of the Founding Fathers of the new American state, and was blind to the imperative need for more market regulation. The forces of global capitalism are much more aggressively anti-egalitarian than Rawls allowed. He seriously underestimated the degree to which typical members of the most powerful groups in society have an especially great need for wealth, power and status. Rawls believed that inequalities in wealth and power would be increasingly levelled down in societies governed by his principles, and in that view he was, I think, right. But if we are intent on maximising the prospects of the least advantaged, as Rawls believed we should be, then this can only be at the expense of those who, by our definition, have too much already. The excessive inequalities that are historically associated with under-regulated capitalism will be defended by those who have the wealth and power. A society governed by Rawls' principles is only made possible through struggle, determination, clear vision – and democratic control of our society and state institutions."

Pilgrim reached out with his other hand and held the Interpreter by both arms. "So now we have the vision of the land we want and how to achieve it. The next step is spreading the good news!"

"Ever the evangelist, my dear Pilgrim," the Interpreter laughed. "But you are right. And that brings me to back to the subject of empathy as a weapon of war. You remember our glimpse of the privileged few at play, the village garden party, children and adults enjoying themselves. We are not at war with monsters, but being at war always produces a monstering of the enemy. So since we are not engaged in an armed struggle with the enemy, I suggest we try the strategy of empathy in order to avoid being sucked into monstering. Treat the 0.1%, the 1%, the fractional enemy, as the devil incarnate and they will behave like monsters. But treat them with understanding, under the protection that a liberal democracy affords you, and they may struggle more than you might imagine. Enwrap them with simple and straightforward accounts of why they think and say and act as they do. Explain the context of their lives, their wealth, their background and their networks. All those who understand the danger they pose to a healthy liberal democracy need to sing from the same sheet on this. They need to be reiterating at every opportunity: 'We know why you are saying this. We know why you are doing that. You can't help yourselves, can you? You can't see how you are hurting people, can you? You have become so good at deceiving yourself, haven't you? Really, we feel almost sorry for you. Do you ever wake up at night and wonder – *Have I got it right; do I really believe my own rhetoric, my own ideology?*

"There has to be a measure of unified and concerted action to bring more and more people in this nominal democracy into an ever-fuller understanding of how global market forces are working with the less attractive basic instincts of humankind to maximise wealth and power at the expense of the mass of humanity. There will be walls of resistance; there will be media manipulation of this message of empathy. But a tidal wave of pointed empathy, intent on ridiculing what is at best self-deception and at worst a much more unpleasant naked greed, would be an unprecedented political phenomenon. I recommend it to you, dear Pilgrim."

Pilgrim was about to express his agreement with the proposal when the sudden sound of dogs barking outside, and the glimpse of probes of infrared night lights through the curtains, forced the two of them to their feet.

"More evasive action, Pilgrim. Hold my arms."

No sooner had the Interpreter spoken than the door was smashed down and four security men stormed in. But the room was now empty.

Pilgrim Discovers the Limits of Empathy

Pilgrim rose from his chair at the desk on which his black digital box resided. He had been immersed in research for hours. This had become the pattern of his days since the Interpreter had spirited the two of them away from the clutches of the security forces. After their escape, he had found himself alone on the road again, next to a turning that he followed until he came to a cottage where he was greeted by a man and woman, who were clearly unsurprised at his arrival. They assured him he would be safe and well cared for with them, and could spend as long as he wanted in uninterrupted study. They were only too pleased to help him on his journey. And so it had been for over a week; Pilgrim making his progress in this contemporary age in front of a digital screen.

As Pilgrim rose, he knew without doubt what he now must do. The next stage of his journey was set. He had to return to the bridge that he had refused to cross earlier in his journey, the bridge that led to the cottage of Well-Being where the man with the polished ebony stick resided; the man called No Benefit. The Interpreter had warned him not to accept any invitation to enter the cottage then, but now all was different. Then he had still been under instruction, a novice in understanding. Now he was seasoned, not a master yet, but knowing enough to no longer be at risk. And this time it was not a matter of invitations. The man who lived in the cottage of Well-Being had questions to answer. Pilgrim was intent on an examination and a first trial of empathy as a weapon of war. Inwardly, Pilgrim was sublimating the anger that had grown layer by layer, day by day, as he learned more and more about the operations of No Benefit's department where his ideas were implemented.

And so it came about that, later that day, Pilgrim found himself again at the bridge that led to the cottage of Well-Being, facing a familiar figure in tweeds and boots. Pilgrim spoke first.

"The time has come for us to talk together, Minister – if I may call you by the name your subordinates use – about those welfare reform policies you were proudly explaining to me when we last met. I said then I needed to understand much more before we spoke further. I believe I now have that understanding. I would like to talk through a number of points with you. Shall we proceed?"

Pilgrim indicated with a confident sweep of his hands the cottage behind No Benefit, with its open door and glimpses of comfort and warmth inside. No Benefit seemed a little unsure what to make of this determined approach from a man he had been warned needed careful and calculated attention. He had, after all, heard Pilgrim use the 'D' word – deception – even on that first visit when Pilgrim had refused his invitation to enter and rest for a while in the cottage. But the minister, to use Pilgrim's chosen name, quickly recovered.

"Come, Pilgrim, and enjoy the hospitality my family and I pride ourselves on. This way to our humble abode."

Pilgrim soon found himself in a luxurious armchair, sitting opposite the minister, both of them drinking tea and eating cake from a trolley that had almost instantly appeared, brought into the room by an elegant lady the minister introduced as his wife, who departed as quickly as she had arrived.

"So what are these pressing matters that you wish to share with me, my friend?" No Benefit asked.

Pilgrim remembered the spirit of empathy and buried the gut response that this man was no friend of his, nor the people who were suffering on his account. Instead, he produced a collection of papers from his pocket, on which he had made a series of notes and pointers in the best tradition of investigative journalism. Another gut feeling had led him to leave the black digital box behind in his lodgings. He had feared for the security of the Interpreter's gift in this unknown territory.

"Minister, I want to press you on some of the documented consequences of your policies. The fact is that your changes to the welfare system have resulted in a massive expansion of food banks. In a land which ranks in the top ten most developed economies in the world there are now, at the end of 2013, more than half a million food banks set up by charitable people who realise that increasing numbers of their fellow citizens are going hungry because they can't make ends meet to provide enough food for themselves or their families. When you came to power in 2010 there were 41,000 food banks. That's a remarkable increase. [87] How do you feel about that?" No Benefit remained silent for a while and then said quietly, "Supply and demand explains much, my friend. We have hardship funds for the really deserving cases who experience genuine misfortune. Do-gooders may actually be making matters worse by creating these food banks. Dependency is a social vice that I'm determined to eliminate. It's our modern scourge. It will be expunged from the body politic, mark my words."

"One quick question, Minister. Do you respect people with expertise?"

"Of course, we politicians do. That's why we surround ourselves with advisors. But you'd be surprised how often so-called experts twist the facts to suit their own political prejudices. So there will be times when I am not always going to find myself in agreement with those who claim to be experts."

"Have you ever twisted facts to suit your prejudices?" Pilgrim asked.

"Being my guest doesn't give you the right to be impertinent, Pilgrim," No Benefit snapped. "We have a mission to save people from themselves, and we will do all that it takes to fulfil our duty in these matters."

"I fear you will, Minister. Look, I have here the conclusions from a report commissioned by your government and written by a team of academic food policy experts. You received this report in the summer of 2013. It only saw the light of day in February 2014, a few weeks ago. Let's not mince words. You and your colleagues suppressed its findings. Why? Because these experts that you commissioned contradicted your claim that you've just repeated: that the rise in the number of food banks is linked to the law of supply and demand. What they actually said was that low income, unemployment and benefit delays have combined to trigger a rise in the demand for food banks." [88]

"You people are all the same," No Benefit scoffed. "You can't see the big picture. You just don't get what we are determined to do here. We have a return-to-work programme that is succeeding, whereas the do-gooders in the last government failed to break the resistance of the long-term unemployed to getting a job and earning a living. What's more, it's not so much how much you earn but how you spend what you take home. We are taking more and more people out of the taxpaying bracket so they can spend more on what they need, like food, not on things they can't afford, like cigarettes. If there are teething problems at this stage in the implementation of our ideas, it's hardly surprising. No one has had the courage to attempt what we are succeeding in doing. We are ridding this country of the curse of welfare dependency." Pilgrim held the minister's gaze for a few seconds. It was true: No Benefit was not out to deceive him. No Benefit was almost perfectly self-deceiving. He really did have the courage of his misshapen convictions. Pilgrim could not see how a dose of empathy would do anything for a man who had lost his way like this. Only exposure and removal from office through the democratic ballot box would rid the land of this kind of conviction politician.

"So you are saying that your department is acting in the public interest when it sits on reports that are biased against them. Well, your track record in this respect is pretty good and getting better, Minister. My most recent research finding is that only last week it emerged that another report, commissioned by your department from independent experts and ready for publication in September 2013, had been sat on until now. You have spoken of your pride in getting the unemployed back to work. Well, this report into the back-to-work programme that has finally seen the light of day makes pretty disturbing reading. Your scheme was to encourage, through incentives, private contract holders to focus resources on getting the most difficult cases back to work. The report says the project is not working well enough. The focus and priority is still on those who are easiest to place. These cases are creamed off. The difficult ones – those with disabilities or poor health – are just parked. These private contract holders were meant to be paid by results. Clearly the mechanism isn't working. And yet this is the same mechanism being rolled out in health and justice too. The report also says that there is no conclusive evidence that the use of sanctions in job centres is effective in changing behaviours or increasing the likelihood of finding employment. Nor is there evidence that people prefer a life on benefits to being at work. Well over half – nearly 60% – of work programme providers thought the work programme wasn't helping or worse. [89] Isn't that pretty damning?"

The minister looked through Pilgrim, and smiled patiently.

"The reality is that the work programme *is* working, my dear Pilgrim. We are doing more than ever before to drive up performance. Your reports don't capture present advances and adjustments."Pilgrim at that moment decided that this exercise in empathy needed to be brought to a close. He got up without a word and left the room. Within a minute or two, he was moving rapidly away from the cottage of Well-Being. This time, the figure of the gentleman farmer came only as far as the stable door, and rather than brandishing his stick in a fit of pique, No Benefit contented himself with a soft, gentle twist of his fingers around its polished neck.

PILGRIM COMES TO
SOME CONCLUSIONS

The Interpreter moved effortlessly and silently beside Pilgrim as together they ascended a hill whose summit lay a good distance away. Pilgrim expanded the question he had just asked.

"Tell me, please. How can I continue to feel empathy towards someone like the minister when his actions lead to so much hurt and harm, and he is so self-deceiving that he cannot recognise any truth other than his own?" The Interpreter stopped and turned towards Pilgrim.

"I'm thinking how best to answer you, Pilgrim. I think you are right to highlight how difficult it is in practice not to monster someone who is behaving in ways that lead to people suffering. But I still believe in the potential power of collective empathy. We can use it almost as a weapon of shame. There are limits to what one person's exercise of empathy can achieve, but if we act together in a unified front to explain to those who are causing the suffering why they are so attached to the free-market ideology and so determined to limit the state, and why they are so unable to hear the cries of those they are hurting, if we do that together then there is more than a chance that they will be just a little disconcerted. And those who vote will be quite a lot more enlightened. You can hear that I am already identifying with the forces gathering in the opposition tents in the Election Fair for next year's carnival. You, we – all of us who have an understanding of what is at stake in these matters, in this democratic rite of a general election, need to be open to any fresh ways of managing the power of Mammon and the pull of the selfish capitalist." [90]

Pilgrim nodded. "The selfish capitalist – yes, I like that phrase. It reminds me of the tale of the selfish giant from my childhood. That had a good ending, of course. The giant saw the error of his ways and found salvation."

"All myths have a core of truth, dear Pilgrim. We can hope." The Interpreter smiled. "Tell me – do you miss the presence of the Lady Hope now? Do you yearn for the return of Charity in that blaze of crimson red and honey yellow, the bird of paradise?"

"Yes – and no. Of course I can't help but remember how good it was to know that the Lady Hope was beside me in person, and as for Charity – well, to know that she once was my salvation fills me with love and thankfulness. But I understand more and more the purpose of my present journey. My task is to emerge ever more knowing about the nature of Mammon and the threat those forces pose for the movement that has seen more and more people matter in the world. Democracy is in its infancy and may yet be strangled, but the more of us who understand what is at stake here, the more chance there is of nurturing it into adult life. We need to disseminate our understanding of what the forces of Mammon have to gain by manipulating democracy and squeezing from it any true meaning. I had no faith to guide me on this journey other than my own belief in the need to search for truth and find a better and kinder world. At this stage of my journey, I feel I will be even stronger if I carry my sense of hope within myself, and if I can be, insofar as this is possible, charity personified. My guides were there to help me through my growing up. Once I am an adult, I will have assimilated their wisdom into my being." The Interpreter hesitated for a moment only, and then remarked quietly, "My time is perhaps drawing to a close, too."

"I hope not," said Pilgrim. "I still have so many questions left to ask! For instance, I'm still left amazed and frustrated and angry that more people are not turning against this present government, and I don't really understand how this can be so. I know what you have taught me and what I have discovered for myself. I know about the growing distrust for all politicians. I know about the degree of manipulation of public opinion by those in power through what they choose to say and how they present themselves. But the story that has been unearthed for me is so telling in whatever field we might look. In welfare, in health, in education – in all three great offices of state, the tale is so disturbing, the fruits so dismal, the deception so apparent, how can there not be a cry of 'Enough!'?"

Pilgrim's stride quickened to match the pace of his thoughts and the intensity of his feelings. They were now very near the summit of the hill they were ascending. Pilgrim continued, his question left in the air.

"In a way, I know the answer to my own question but it is not one I really want to hear or acknowledge. It seems people in the mass will be shaped by what they take to be good news. Or rather, more accurately, what is presented to them as 'good news'. And that good news is felt in the purse. I've been aware ever since I've had our digital box that Pocket Money and his team have been boasting about how the country is beginning an economic recovery. During 2013, there were encouraging signs for the government. Unemployment figures were down, so too were the indicators for inflation, consumers were spending more, the housing market was recovering."

"And is that believable, given our analysis to date?" the Interpreter asked.

"Economies do recover in time, whatever governments do. We're in the top ten in the world, still. But a range of economic analysts have been quick to point out the real limits to this improvement. The housing boom has been engineered by this government to stimulate the economy. There is a strong risk that it will produce a housing bubble that bursts. The increase in consumer spending must be due largely to people dipping into their savings as confidence begins to return, because in the big picture there have not been the increments in living standards that come from rising incomes. There is an absence of pay increases that outstrip inflation and lead to a genuine sense of being better off. Only when people are being paid more and feeling genuinely better off will industry and commerce respond with decisions to invest the capital that's waiting for just such an upturn in confidence. So no – there are good reasons for being wary of the claim that all is now well." [91]

"You are right to be wary," said the Interpreter. "But many people in our democracy seem to be swayed by the thought that there is a genuine recovery—"

Pilgrim interrupted, reaching at the same time into his pocket for the notes that he had recorded from his digital trawls.

"Do you know, a couple of months ago opinion polls were showing – let me see – that the government were fifteen percentage points ahead of the Labour party on the question: *Who do you trust to run the economy?* [92] Last week, a poll showed that Labour support had slumped to its lowest level since 2010. They now had a lead of just one percentage point over the Conservatives: 33% to 32%. A year ago they were ten points ahead. But the Tories have been higher. In 2012, the same poll had the Tories on 38% and Labour on 36%. The rise of UKIP is clearly now a factor. They are on 15% and must be taking more voters away from the Tories than Labour. [93] We end up being grateful for small mercies that may yet be critical. But why can't more people see the harm being done and the hurt being suffered?"

Pilgrim indicated with his spare hand an underlining on the notepad he was holding.

"Look. Here I've recorded the fact that earlier this month, an international organisation, the OECD, warned that poverty will become ever more entrenched in Britain if the government doesn't maintain social spending to protect the most vulnerable. Rising inequality and social divisions are likely to continue to increase unless action is taken. [94] And here there's a report from the charity Oxfam, revealing the scale of Britain's growing inequality. It's called *A Tale of Two Britains*. It says that the poorest 20% in the UK – around 12.5 million people – have wealth totalling just over £28 billion, an average of £2,230 each. The five top entries on the UK rich list by themselves had property, savings and other assets worth as much: £28 billion. The most affluent family in Britain, headed by Major General Gerald Grosvenor, has more wealth than the poorest 10% of the population – around 6.25 million people. Why? Real wages are falling. Food and fuel costs have risen faster than incomes. Most poor people don't own homes or shares. [95] And does this government of millionaires care?"

"The human species does have an extraordinary facility for turning a blind eye and a deaf ear when it suits," the Interpreter explained. "We are left with the conundrum of explaining two things.

"First, why there is not a direct appeal by the leaders of the Labour opposition to those who have the vote among the 12.5 million poorest fifth? 'We understand your pain and your anger. We feel it with you. Here is our account of how and why things have got this bad. We will change the way our economy and society work so your interests are protected. So you are not used and abused.'

"Secondly, why there is not a direct appeal to all those in the electorate who believe in fairness and decency? 'Here is the story of how matters have reached this pass. If you believe that people matter and we've gone way past what is tolerable in demonising and rubbishing millions of the poorest and most vulnerable, vote for us: the party that believes in truth and justice.'

"A John Rawls touch at the end. Enough to suggest the seemingly unspeakable: the other main party, the dominant party of government, believes in lies and injustice. The price of wealth for the few."

The Interpreter and Pilgrim paused on their journey. They had reached the summit of the hill. Below them, they could now see, stretched out before them, the multi-coloured canvas patchwork of tent tops covering the acres given over to the Election Fair. There was just over a year until the election itself. Pilgrim turned to the Interpreter and sighed.

"You're right. That's a price no one should have to pay."

PILGRIM RECEIVES SOLACE FROM HOPE AND THE DIGITAL BOX

The Election Fair had been dismantled some weeks previously and the site bulldozed by men in machines, working on zero-hour contracts and employed by a subcontractor running construction and demolition operations for the company that was a subsidiary of the private equity group that now controlled swathes of the nation's schools, prisons and hospitals. A year is a very long time in politics, and Pilgrim was still in a state of shock. The Lady Hope rested beside him as he sat slumped on the bench at the top of the hill that overlooked the site of the Election Fair below, cleared of rubble and razor wire-fenced for the next five years.

The Lady Hope spoke softly.

"Remember, for as long as I am with you there will always be light at the end of the tunnel. You can already take some comfort from your prescience. Your growing understanding of the battle between the forces of Mammon and our real needs was never wrong. You should never doubt the insights of your journey over the last five years."Pilgrim sighed. For the past year he had been his own independent observer and researcher. This had been the very spot where the Interpreter had bid him farewell, assuring Pilgrim that he was now knowing enough to continue without his assistance.

The digital box would provide the data he required. Pilgrim now had sufficient of the gift of interpretation not to need his presence. And it was true. Pilgrim had learned so much. With the election itself looming nearer and nearer the future had looked as if was going to be brighter. The days of spinning and deceiving government ministers seemed numbered.

The opinion polls had all pointed to a general election result on 7th May 2015 that would be too close to call. Nearly everyone agreed that a hung parliament was the most likely outcome. The people were seeing through the lies and deceptions – or at least enough of them were to deny the Bullingdon boys another five years of power. The neo-liberal Conservative party agenda would be cast aside.[96] How gut-wrenchingly wrong. There was now a new Conservative government with an overall majority. [97] The country was facing five more years of austerity, with more dramatic reductions in the size and responsibilities of the state. Pilgrim feared that eventually there would be social mayhem. Community ties would be stretched to breaking point. And all with a mandate that had the blessing of democracy.

The Lady Hope was reading his thoughts.

"We were all taken aback by the power of the meme that Mammon had been conjuring for so long. And there is one special lesson to learn. Never to underestimate the forces of Mammon and their determination to cling to wealth and power."

Pilgrim nodded.

"Looking back now with the gift of hindsight, I can see how long-term their strategy was – I know that even before the 2010 general election the Tories were laying the blame for the banking crash at the door of the Labour party in government. I've discovered how that message was drilled into the public consciousness at every opportunity by every Conservative politician as soon as they opened their mouth to speak. It was as if they had been reduced to robotic beings by their party machine. And every Conservative-supporting media outlet repeated the same refrain – 85% of the press reflected that outlook.[98] 'You can't trust the Labour Party with the economy. You know you can trust a Tory government to look after your interests. *Our* interests.'

"It has been such a deception. Every economist worth their salt recognises that the economic crash of 2008 was a banking crisis, first and foremost, and that the Labour government actually handled the crisis with considerable skill.[99] If ever there was a case of mud sticking…"

"Quite," said Hope. "The need now is to meet deceit with truth. How do you think that can best be done?"

"Well, we can certainly start by avoiding the mistake of the Labour party in opposition over the last five years. Their strategic approach seemed to be to never look back and never bother to address and refute the lies and deceptions. Their leader chose to make that his and his party's default position. [100] You talk of the meme that was at work as people voted. You're right. In the end, the notion that your needs and your family's were more likely to be met by voting Conservative satisfied the imagination of enough voters to explain the outcome."

"Their hopes were misplaced?"

"You know they were! The Conservatives kept insisting that the government's long-term economic plan was working. But it was failing in both theory and practice. Such growth as there has been has relied on over-stimulating the housing market. They boast about halving the deficit when the plan

125

was to eliminate it. Manufacturing and construction are still operating at pre-2008 levels. There has been the first fall in living standards over a five-year period since records began in 1960. Close on a million people are relying on food banks. [101] How can you call that success?"

"Do you think the people who voted Conservative did not know all this?" Hope asked.

"The more I find out, the more I'm convinced that the answer lies in the power of the repetition of the lie," said Pilgrim. "This is war by propaganda. If you, as a politician, keep repeating your story and presenting it as the truth and most of the media support you and the opposition don't offer a convincing alternative, you can get away with it." [102]

"So we need a convincing alternative?"

"Of course! But we can't make sense of what happened without understanding that Scotland provides a crucial part of the solution to the puzzle. I realise more and more that my journey reveals different paths in the countries and even the regions that make up this state that calls itself the United Kingdom. I'm not sure that the Interpreter, when he was guiding me, had ever focused on the issue of Scotland. I found out for myself through the digital box all about the referendum to decide the issue of independence for Scotland. [103] But it wasn't until the last stages of the general election campaign itself that I grasped two facts. One, what a difference a capable, charismatic and experienced political leader makes, and two, that this party – the SNP – that represented the interests of those who wanted independence also identified itself with outright opposition to austerity. [104] The SNP was telling a convincing true story about the economy. The Labour party declined to do so."

Pilgrim turned to face the Lady Hope. "So how do you meet deceit with truth? You follow the example of the SNP. My God, didn't Labour suffer as a result of their failure to honour the truth?! They lost all but one of their MPs in Scotland. [105] That devastating tidal wave of disgust north of the border is for me the most powerful meme operating in the state on 7th May."

Pilgrim had become quite animated. He was now standing and speaking with the conviction of an orator.

"And then we need to think more carefully about how an opposition party ends up with a leader who can inspire the confidence of enough people to ensure that he or she is not projected as a reason for voting for the government. The message was clear enough. 'Do you seriously see this man being respected as our PM by other world leaders?' The Tories in power systematically and consistently set about rubbishing the plausibility of the leader of the Labour party from the moment he was elected. [106] He was a decent man – but mud sticks, doesn't it? Sow the seeds of doubt often enough and some will take root." [107]

The Lady Hope beckoned him to sit down beside her on the bench once more.

"You remember my story of Lizzie? How I became her at the times of her need? She and I have done more than just survive. Hope will always crush doubt. She is now a leader in her own community, campaigning to protect those who have been left victims of a ruthless system that lacks compassion. You have not forgotten the extraordinary No Benefit, have you?"

"Who could?!" Pilgrim exclaimed.

"Other single mothers began to notice her in the street and at the gates of the nursery. A few months before the election, Lizzie took the decision to join her local Labour party and became one of their keenest activists. Like you, she was dumbstruck by the Conservative election victory in May. But after a month or so, she began to recover her vitality as the local branch began to turn its attention to the issue of the new national leader to replace the unfortunate Ed Miliband. Now that brings us up-to-date. A breath of hope came last week. [108] That is a story still to unfold in the future, which, as you know, is as closed to me as it is to you. Yet I can't help but feel that something rather extraordinary is around the corner."

Pilgrim looked thoughtful.

"You mean there's now a chance that we'll have an opposition leader who'll have the charisma and appeal of someone like Nicola Sturgeon in Scotland? That would be extraordinary! But nothing I've uncovered in the digital box over the last year suggests that is at all likely. Who in the Labour party could possibly match her achievements?"

"We will see. Cometh the moment, cometh the woman – or man. But for this moment, this present time, tell me more about your discoveries in the box of facts – the digital treasure trove from which you draw your interpretations and conclusions. Tell me particularly about the findings that make you cheerful. That fill you with hope."

"With pleasure!" Pilgrim said. "When I look back over that first year of independence from the Interpreter's guidance, I remember being so thrilled when I came across articles and books that had been written by those who seemed to share my concerns, and had now reached conclusions that supported the insights I'd already developed. I know there are dangers here. I might be closing my mind to any ideas other than those that reinforce my own prejudices. But I hope by now I have had sufficient training and acquired enough experience to be aware of the peril, and I trust my judgement. So here are some of the ideas and writings that seem to me to undermine the fortress of Mammon and his servants. Thomas Piketty's *Capital in the Twenty-First Century*. That's right at the top of my list. [109] One month before the general election, it had shot to the top of the Amazon bestseller list in the United States. In nearly seven hundred pages he marshals the evidence that we are on a one-way highway to inequality unless action is taken. The Frenchman's most powerful argument is simple. In an economy where the rate of return on capital outstrips the rate of growth, inherited wealth will always grow faster than earned wealth. We've got a global-wide slow-growth economy alongside financial returns that are recovering well from the 2008 crash. The rising wealth of the 1%, the growing level of inequality, and the consequent threats to social democracy and social justice are inescapable facts unless something is done to avert this trend."

Pilgrim's gaze was fixed on the scene below him, the razor-wired and rubble-cleared stadium of the Election Fair. What role would – and could – Election Fairs play in the future? He buried the thought and continued.

"Piketty has shattered the basis for the belief that many economists shared that inequality becomes less as capitalist societies become more mature. It doesn't. What may have been true for much of the last century is no longer so. Demographics and the movement of people across borders are leading to lower wages for many. So is the weakening of trade unions. So is the election of governments that want low rates of taxation – all these factors help explain the reinforcement of this economic thrust towards inequality."

The Lady Hope interrupted.

"And where will we find the hope in all this?"

"Understanding what's going on has to be, by itself, a reason for optimism, doesn't it? And then Piketty is not afraid to say what needs to be done. There has to be redistribution to lessen inequality, but we can't do it simply through taxes on income as we used to. Now there has to be, in effect, confiscation of wealth, not just income. [110]

"Is it possible or just pie in the sky? It will be a battle, but this is a struggle to determine the soul of society itself on our planet. Yes, I'm hopeful. If we're not, we might as well roll over and have done with it. This struggle is what being a pilgrim should be all about. Look what happened in Scotland: almost half the people voting for a party that wants an end to austerity and independence from a right-wing government in England. [111] If we can create the awareness, our shared sense of justice and fairness will triumph over the forces of self-interest. I remember what I learned about John Rawls from the Interpreter. And Piketty is not the only voice warning of the dangers of growing inequality. Even the conservative IMF – the International Monetary Fund – has come to similar conclusions when it compared different countries' growth. Countries that experience more economic growth have lower levels of inequality. [112] And yet another voice is the economist who won the Nobel Prize in 2001, Joseph Stiglitz. He is one of the most influential critics of economic and political inequality. In his latest book, *The Great Divide*, he shows how the chasm between the rich and the poor has grown even larger in the United States and elsewhere since 2008. And, he argues, that is morally wrong and economically foolish. [113] I read a newspaper interview he gave just after the election in which he criticised Ed Miliband for his lack of vision and too-narrow focus. He poured scorn on the idea that the UK economy was recovering well. He said we've had nearly a decade of almost zero growth. Productivity is poor, middle incomes are stagnating. [114] I noted down the concluding words of the journalist who did the interview..."

Pilgrim reached into his pocket and produced another digital tool that he had acquired. "Here they are: *It just needs someone to take Stiglitz's basic finding that inequality, quite apart from being bad for the poor, is bad for growth, and then convey it to the public at large in a manner that speaks to people's conscience and aspiration. Whoever is left in the running for the Labour party leadership should get reading.* [114] There's my good reason for being hopeful. We can appeal to the people's sense of fairness and justice – and to their legitimate desire for their rightful slice of the cake."

"Empathy alongside self-interest," said the Lady Hope. "Yes, I see hope in that."

"The more I've read," Pilgrim continued, "the more I've come to understand that if we are going to drag ourselves out of the clutches of Mammon, we need to reveal to everyone what those who have power and wealth are doing. Because, make no mistake, it is against the self-interests of the vast majority. I've read enough to know that the future will very soon bring a new agenda whereby the idea of growth itself on our planet will have to be reassessed. But for now, our first concern should be with establishing the mechanisms for achieving a fairer distribution of the fruits of the market – and that can't but stand us in good stead for whatever the future brings..."

Pilgrim hesitated for a moment as he sought to find the right words to communicate what was in his mind.

"I feel… I feel now that the way people used to talk about the battle between capitalism and socialism is no longer helpful. Too many sane and compassionate people who have an understanding of economics that is the opposite of the neo-liberal nonsense we are suffering believe in the proven power of the market to generate wealth. But that market has to have a measure of regulation to control it, otherwise Mammon will rule. Inequalities of wealth and power will be the order of the day. There is a professor who teaches economics at Cambridge University, Ha-Joon Chang, who is very clear about both the advantages of capitalism and the need to regulate it." [115]

Pilgrim checked the digital notebook in his hand. "This is what Chang says: *Being pro-business doesn't – and shouldn't – mean leniency towards illegal or semi-legal activities by business people and companies, as some Tory party donors and right-wing newspapers want it to mean… When unscrupulous business people break the basic rules of competition, whether it is rigging foreign exchange markets or not paying the minimum wage, they are hurting the rest of the business community… What we need is a genuinely pro-business government, which has a clear economic strategy that recognises different business interests and priorities, while reconciling those with the interests and values of other members of society.*" [116]

A smile appeared on Pilgrim's face. "I like discovering the sound and reasoned views of independent academics. Their voices are not yet heard by the mass of the people because of the way the media works, but truth will out. Here's another gem that I relished when I came across it. It is a letter signed by seventy-eight academics, headed by Ha-Joon Chang, Thomas Piketty and David Blanchflower. Listen to this attack on George Osborne's economic understanding. *The chancellor's plans, announced in his Mansion House speech, for "permanent budget surpluses"... have no basis in economics... If the government chooses to try to inflexibly run surpluses, and therefore no longer borrow, the knock-on effect to the rest of the economy will be significant... The plan actually takes away one of the central purposes of modern government: to deliver a stable economy in which all can prosper.* [117]

"That's telling them! But they know already. They are not fools. They are manipulators, and for them the mass of the people are ever ripe for peeling."

The smile had gone. Pilgrim was angry. "It is the patronising contempt for ordinary people that gets to me. We are all equal in worth. There should not be this reckless pursuit of deception. I remember being so shocked when I discovered the story of phone-hacking during my first researches using the digital black box. [118] I know now that Andy Coulson was found guilty at his trial. Others were seen as innocent in law by the jury. In other words, the guilty ones were, it seems, deceiving even their colleagues and bosses, whose defence was that they did not know what was going on. [119] Wherever you look, there is deception. I said at the time when I first found out the details of this extraordinary business that these are not matters with which a Prime Minister in a healthy democracy should be associated. Yet Cameron made Coulson his Head of Communications in 2012. As I said before, he must have been spinning very hard for so little of that mess to be left sticking to him. But spinning and deception are the very substance of a world shaped by Mammon. I see it in the press. I see it in politics. There should be no surprise that there are links."

Pilgrim paused. "If the opposite of hope is despair, then there are times when I feel close to despair. I admit it. But none of us can afford to avoid our responsibility in all this. I find myself a pilgrim again because I was moved by the suffering I saw all around me. I don't fully understand why but I feel that I am destined to be a seeker after truth in order to play my part in alleviating this suffering in whatever place and time I find myself. That is why I need you, my Lady Hope. To breathe fresh life into a soul that can at times feel overburdened. It is tempting to imagine being free of all this concern. I remember the baggage I carried on my back when I began this journey, and those times I was tempted by Mammon to join him, or at least bury my head in self-deception and feigned ignorance. These are the private thoughts I need to acknowledge, confess, even, as I would once have said. But I know what you have promised."

"So do I," said the Lady Hope, "and Hope is true to her word. A life without hope for fairness, justice and equality, a life filled with unnecessary suffering, a life filled with false hopes for more money and power – that is no life. A life without worthwhile hope is a contradiction in terms. It is a hopeless life. It is not a life well lived.

"Come, my dear Pilgrim, embrace me one more time. Our time together must draw to a close for the time being. We are coming ever nearer to the end of this particular pilgrimage. We will meet again after Her Majesty's Opposition has elected their new leader, and we will see what hope there may be in that event."

Pilgrim's Journey Comes to an End

Hope had drawn Pilgrim closer in the conference room that overlooked the Thames hundreds of feet below. In the security of their mezzanine viewing point, they remained unseen and unknowable to the assembled boardroom members seated beneath them – business-suited, grave men, unsmiling, and amongst them a scattering of determined, made-up women. But the sense of menace was pressing. Pilgrim shivered. And then he saw them rise, all of them, as if one. A solitary figure had appeared through a door at the end of the room and was now taking his place behind the vacant seat at the head of the table. A man in his late thirties, tanned and athletically elegant, dressed this time in a Savile Row-suited style. Unlike the first time, when Pilgrim had met him in the small marquee in the centre of Vanity Fair, the figure that Hope had explained was Mammon himself remained now, as his underlings, unsmiling.

Pilgrim could feel the sting of sweat in his armpits. His eyes turned towards those of Hope in search of reassurance. The Lady Hope drew him closer still and spoke with quiet authority.

"You have nothing to fear, dear Pilgrim. You and I remain unseen and unheard. For the present, our world is not their world any more than their world is ours. For over a year, you have been spared direct contact with the force that controls Vanity Fair and his followers in order to pursue your own search for digital knowledge to underpin your new understanding. Now it is time for you to share their company again, but do not fear. You will not need to meet them face-to-face. Not on this pilgrimage, at least. But you will now be a witness, with me, to their deliberations as they consider the latest threat, here in the United Kingdom, to their global manipulation of wealth and power. An event that has brought us hope, as I promised, has produced fear and loathing in them. This they did not expect."

Pilgrim already knew much about the event. He had followed its twists and turns with growing interest through the screen stories of his digital black box. He was beginning to grasp its potential, and now he had the opportunity to see and hear the reactions of those very forces who had the most to lose through this simple twist of fate.

The figure now standing behind the empty chair focused his gaze on the assembly of subordinates. Each of them thrilled to the exquisite fusion of fear and wonder that their master evoked in them. Hail to their champion! This man, this extraordinary icon, who was able to feed on their insecurities and end up gifting them so much; yet leaving them with an exquisite, insatiable craving for more. And more.

"My lord, I must confess that I am at a loss as to how to make sense of what has happened. Do we now have cause to be concerned, when all seemed to be proceeding so admirably?"

Pilgrim gasped involuntarily. The tweeds and boots had been replaced by the tailored suit, but there was no doubt. The figure who had just spoken was none other than the person he had known as No Benefit, bereft of his polished ebony stick. Pilgrim stared more closely still, trying to discern the other faces of the figures seated around the table. Goodness! It was true. He had met numbers of them before on his journey. The Team Leader and his barman, Pocket Money; Alfred Price; the Headmaster; even Postmutin and Vladi Onkov. They were all there, and others he had never seen before, assembled before their leader. Pilgrim caught his breath. A third figure had appeared unseen on the balcony and was holding his other arm, very firmly. It was the Interpreter, and his familiar voice was now whispering in Pilgrim's ear.

"We live in interesting times, my dear Pilgrim. There is a sense of things coming to a head, is there not? For better or worse, depending on your position in relation to these matters."

The Interpreter moved in front of Pilgrim and placed his hands on Pilgrim's shoulders as if in an act of benediction. The Lady Hope had eased gently to one side, exchanging the briefest of tender glances with the Interpreter, who continued.

"First, very quickly, my congratulations on the quality of your research. I applaud your conclusions. But we have much to learn from the events below, as well as from the events that have triggered this extraordinary meeting. We must listen very carefully."

Below them, the figure addressed as 'my lord' was now seated at the head of the table. The words of Mammon, spoken with the same calm confidence that Pilgrim remembered from the first Vanity Fair, were clear and precise. But now there was more ice in the delivery.

"Concern is too strong a term, my friend. Let us say only that we must remain vigilant and take steps to deal with any developments that could be contrary to the interests of the enterprise. We must continue to ensure that all our regular procedures are followed to the letter in order to minimise the adverse effects of this little local difficulty. That is why you have been called together for this gathering.

"We are talking here of the unexpected election of a sixty-seven-year-old nonentity to the leadership of Her Majesty's Opposition in the United Kingdom. A figure of wry amusement, and now concern, to the overwhelming majority of his fellow Labour party Members of Parliament, whom we have firmly yoked to our agenda. [120] They are, after all, happy on board our Wealth Is Health train."

There were ripples of applause around the table at the sound of the familiar slogan. Their leader silenced the interruption with a single slight movement of his hand and continued.

"In five years when the next Election Fair arrives in town, he will, we assume, be reduced to the same kind of memory-dust as the leaders who failed to grasp the reins of the Conservative party after the fall of the Magnificent One whom they knew as the Iron Lady. [121] This ageing anachronism, this crypto-Marxist relic from the last century, is no man of steel."

The insult went down very well all around the table. Postmutin and Onkov seemed particularly amused. [122] Their leader's hand brought them back to order.

"It seems inconceivable that there should be any fate for him other than oblivion. He has the full backing of only handfuls of party MPs, the electorate had barely heard of him, and we now have the usual saturation spraying of scorn and distrust by every media outlet under our control. Even those media that are not always so friendly to us seem minded to join in on our side." [123]

Mammon's tone became more emphatic still. "But I will not say I am wholly comfortable. This man, this upstart Mr Corbyn… Jeremy…" Mammon articulated the sound of the forename as if it were primordial slime "…has enjoyed his short-term victory on the back of a movement, a meme as they say these days, that we all know is apparent elsewhere in the world. We've dealt with the threat in Greece,[124] we are on top of the situation in Spain,[125] we will see off the danger in the United States.[126] But the fact that it has surfaced here in the United Kingdom is irritating when we had made such headway. The Conservative party had been returned as the natural rulers of your beloved democracy. Its leaders are a splendid mixture of free-thinkers, the purest of their kind. Indeed, we have the pleasure of the company of the best of their top stars around this very table. Gentlemen, I salute you."

There were appreciative murmurings.

"And we had Her Majesty's Opposition largely in the bag too. So no, it is not a matter of major concern. But it is an irritant. One we could do without."

Pilgrim could see that the figure he recognised as the Headmaster had his hand up. Mammon indicated that he was free to speak. Pilgrim watched as the Headmaster, who, he recalled, was also known as Dull Mind, a man without the full wiring in his being, rose from his chair and addressed his own master.

"My lord, I do of course agree wholeheartedly with your brilliant summary of the matter that is before us. It is no more than an irritant. But as you wisely say, it is one we could do without. A minor concern, dare I say. Indeed, it has not escaped my attention that one of our own brethren – who I believe has sent his sincere apologies for his unavoidable absence today – has already warned of the dangers of underestimating Mr Corbyn. He has, I believe, even gone so far as to suggest that it is not certain that a Mr Corbyn-led Labour party would lose at the next Election Fair if we were to have another recession… if our present government became very unpopular. [127] These thoughts were perhaps best left unexpressed, but…"

The tension in the room below had become palpable. The hand of Mammon rose to silence the Headmaster whose expression suggested he realised he had made a misjudgement. Mammon spoke, even as Dull Mind slid back into his seat.

"Our worthy Headmaster has decided to draw our attention to what he might have called, if he had the inclination, a worst-case scenario. I am grateful to him…"

The Headmaster shifted uncomfortably in his chair. He seemed, to Pilgrim from above, to shrink a little. Mammon's calm, steady delivery continued, with a cutting edge crafted to the insecurities of each attendee.

"…As I am sure we all are. A little speculation can sometimes be fruitful. Too much, though, can land the gamester in serious trouble. As we all know."

The Headmaster clenched his buttocks. Mammon was looking straight through him as he continued.

"So let me explain precisely why we have nothing to fear if we employ all our usual weaponry, and if we all believe in our own inalienable right to continue exercising our power in our interests. Because, as we all know, that power serves the interests of all in society. Where would they be without us?"

A murmur of self-appreciation rippled through the brethren.

"First, we continue to enjoy overall command of the media. The press and the television and radio channels are largely on our side. The Corbyn phenomenon is seen – and presented – as radical and maverick. Outside the Scottish part of this realm, we have effectively shaped a nation to favour individualism and lean towards conservatism. They will instinctively cling to nurse for fear of something worse." Nods of approval greeted this judgement.

"Half a million or more rebels we can cope with. We can tolerate that degree of deviance. Indeed, we can turn it to our advantage. Rebellion. Deviance. They mean fear. That fear will breathe fresh life into the forces that were behind our election triumph. The fear that control of the economy will fall into the wrong hands – incompetent Labour hands. The fear that control of our political destiny in this insecure world will fall into the hands of weak men, masquerading as leaders – the limp Miliband and now Jester Corbyn. Oh, we'll have a field day exploiting the threat posed by half a million Corbyn supporters. Yes, bring it on! One million, two million Corbynistas – the more the merrier. We will turn the fantasies that shape the aspirations of twenty million anxious voters into nightmares." The table resounded with the thuds of beating fists, pummelling into the dark, polished oak.

"The Left is dead. Washed up. The individual is the kitemark of the new order in the 21st century, not the solidarity of 19th century socialism. The future lies with those who aspire for what is rightfully theirs through hard work and self-discipline." Mammon focused precisely on the bowed head of the Headmaster.

"It may be that the economy will be slower to recover due to global forces beyond the control of our government. [128] In that case, the last thing decent, hardworking people need is an experiment in government by a bunch of radical amateurs who don't understand the business world. I really see no reason why this government, represented so handsomely around this table, should ever lose its popularity as long as it holds steady and continues to pull the levers of power and influence as it has been taught to do."

The figure of Mammon eased himself into his chair. The applause was rapturous.

A smaller, and on closer inspection somewhat older, member of the gathering rose almost immediately from his chair. It was Postmutin. Pilgrim observed that the glimmerings of a smile had formed for the first time on Mammon's tanned face. The head of the table evidently approved this bold action. Mammon pressed a button on the electronic pad that he took from his pocket and the room was filled with the sound of an almost instant translation from the speaker's native Russian.

"Gentlemen – and ladies – permit me to say how delighted I am to be able to join you for this most absorbing meeting. We have our differences but they are far outweighed by our common concerns, not least this Corbyn matter. Our leader is, of course, correct. The Corbyn meme will be short-lived. But we have much to learn from it. I have been most struck by the issue of the finger on the button. I mean the nuclear button. It is of course vital that we all continue to fuel our growth on the back of our military forces. We all stand to gain from protecting our peoples from external threats. We need our enemies!"

Postmutin paused to sip water from the glass in front of him. The rest of the table sat fascinated.

"We need each other! And we need our nuclear deterrents. I have come to appreciate their extraordinary qualities even more now after your Mr Corbyn said he would never be able to bring himself to press the nuclear button [129] in response to another country's nuclear strike."

Postmutin took another sip from the glass and smiled.

"Like a strike from my country. With my finger on the button! Would I do it, my friends? Would I risk the annihilation of much of the planet on an itchy digit? Would I be that crazy? Perhaps. The gamester in me is rather fascinated by the idea. Most of us would survive in our nuclear bunkers for long enough to see the world again when it was safe. But the infrastructure would be, shall we say, rather depleted. What is certain is that no one can be sure. And in that lies the beauty of our exquisite nuclear weaponry. They provide the perfect justification for spending vast sums of money that might otherwise be used to reduce the very inequalities that keep our wealth and power intact."

Pilgrim could feel a deep respect for this man rising like sweet vapour from his audience.

"The mass of the people are insecure, afraid and needy. The market forces that have made us what we are thrive on that neediness and uncertainty. Those same forces have helped create this unease in the first place. The people have become willing slaves to their insecurities. Who among the masses will risk their own security by turning their backs on a nuclear game that pays out such handsome dividends? It gives them the security of mutually assured destruction, and provides them with the ultimate source of insecurity – the tantalising figure of an enemy who just might be mad enough to press the nuclear button. Listen to them on their chat shows and in their focus groups. They need their enemies. They need the threat. They are hooked."

Postmutin had cut to the quick. "My friends, your Mr Corbyn will never be able to change the minds of enough people to win an election by nailing his colours to the mast of unilateral nuclear disarmament. QED."

The reception from his colleagues was almost as warm as it had been for Mammon himself. Hope and the Interpreter glanced at one another and began to guide Pilgrim back from the balcony overlooking the conference room, drawing him away into the velvet-curtained recess at the back of the room.

Pilgrim felt the now-familiar sensation of being out of his body, and it seemed only seconds later that he was in a small room, bare of furniture apart from the table in the centre and the three chairs on which they now sat, and the wide screen filling one wall. A screen that was relaying live coverage from the very conference that he had just been watching in person. He could see that Head Boy and Pocket Money were standing up together and addressing the meeting. The Interpreter turned a dial on the device in his hand and the volume on the audio link with the screen faded to a distant murmur. He turned to Pilgrim and spoke.

"Know thine enemy! Have you a measure of their strengths and weaknesses? Personally, there is only so much I can stomach at any one sitting. I assume you are, by now, the same?"

"Indeed," replied Pilgrim. "I still find Mammon himself very sinister, but the rest less so. And the arguments they use seem compelling, but their way of seeing the world remains warped. It is an accepted way, I grant you. But it is not the only way, and it is not a good way. It's as if they're shining a light on us and we are revealed as self-centred individuals, huddling together for comfort in collective denial of our own potential for goodness. But I know now that the world and the people in it look so different when illuminated by kindness. They, I think, know this too, deep down. And it scares them. They'll stay in denial and do their best to extinguish any glimmerings of this new light. But they know they are always at a disadvantage because most people are hardwired to enjoy a world in which fairness and decency are celebrated."

"My confidence in you has been well placed!" said the Interpreter. "Yes, and that is why the emergence of Jeremy Corbyn has been so deeply concerning for them. This is a man who has consistently seen the world as a fundamentally good place filled with good people who are shamefully let down by an elite who are half-crazed by power and wealth. He has had only a dozen or so like-minded socialist friends in the party that calls itself the party of labour.[130] Their core principles you know. A new kind of politics. Growth, not austerity. Fair taxes for all. Action in the long-term interest of the planet. Decent homes for all. A foreign policy that prioritises justice and assistance. An end to privatisation in health. The list goes on… [131] These ideas will strike a chord. Tribal Conservatives will always resist, but there are not enough of them to win a general election. There are, though, sufficient millions of ordinary people who will eventually, in the right circumstances, say yes to such a programme."

"And it's already happened in Scotland!"

The Interpreter laughed with pleasure.

"Exactly! Come – let's brace ourselves for some more malice and deception."

The screen images of Head Boy and Pocket Money filled the wall as the three of them turned in the direction of the now-audible voices. Head Boy and Pocket Money were standing together and, so it seemed to Pilgrim, working as a double act, their lines timed effortlessly. They were painting their portrait of the even greater Britain being constructed on the back of their election victory. They were the builders of the new world. They were the natural party of the working man. They were the real politicians you could trust to develop a society of fairness and decency where all pathways led to work and independence – and then on to self-respect and dignity. They were the new party of labour who would make an all-out assault on poverty. [132]

Pilgrim could feel his face redden with anger. Hope and the Interpreter exchanged one of their knowing glances. Intuitively, they sensed this was now the time.

Suddenly, the screen images vanished and then returned, to reveal a room filled with figures diving for cover, chairs thrown aside, suits ripping, bodies scrabbling for safety under the shelter of the table-top. An astonishing light now filled the screen, an intense radiation of energy that transcended every item in that space, animate and inanimate. The sweep of crimson red and honey yellow seemed to dissolve the screen, and for the third time Pilgrim heard the sublime sound of the bird-creature that had promised never to abandon him. Charity was present.

Then there was silence.

Pilgrim stared ahead. He was still looking at the screen on the wall, but he was alone now. He could see the conference table, the chairs scattered around, the aftermath. There was no sign of the members of the board. The illusion lasted only a few seconds. Pilgrim realised that he was now watching the bodies that had burrowed for cover begin to emerge. Mammon was the first to appear. He had brushed himself down and was back sitting at the head of the table before most of his agents had even emerged. Pilgrim continued to watch in fascination. Within a few minutes, all were seated, and their faces remained as they had been before: unsmiling. There was no suggestion that anyone understood why clothing had become torn, skin bruised, hair and makeup dishevelled. There was no sense that anyone was aware at all of what they had experienced. Pilgrim marvelled, not for the first time, at the power of self-deception. Mammon was calling the meeting to order. Pilgrim watched as Head Boy and Pocket Money rose and began again to extol the virtues of hard work in a society that works for all. Everyone in the room had obliterated every trace of the memory of their encounter with Charity. As he grasped ever more fully what it must be like to live a life without real hope or real charity, Pilgrim felt himself once more falling away into another world.

Pilgrim could see three figures ahead of him on the road, and hastened forward in order to catch up with them. So much had happened. His head was still spinning. He had no idea how, but he was back on a dusty road again, his mind filled with images of Mammon and his agents. Try as he might, though, the three figures ahead remained out of reach, always a distance away. They did not at any point look back. He might as well have been alone. After a while, he got used to the idea of not catching up and settled into his own pace. Eventually, he began to feel weary. His day had been long and revealing. He would look for somewhere to rest for the night.

His head filled with the outcomes of his search for truth and understanding, and his heart went out to those whose sufferings had compelled him to take to the road in the first place. He began to recall more clearly another journey, another pilgrimage, in another time. The last thought he remembered was that this modern pilgrimage would have a telling too.

When the figures ahead knew the time was right and they did look back, Pilgrim was no more to be seen. But in the distance, further back still on the same road, they could see the dust rising from the steps of what seemed to be a mass of people. The Interpreter, Hope and Charity exchanged glances and smiled.

REFERENCES

1. Ortiz, Isobel and Anthony, David (2011). *Global Inequality: Beyond the Bottom Billion – A Rapid Review of Income Distribution in 141 Countries.* (A working document produced at the UNICEF Policy and Practice Division, New York.) The authors conclude (p. 45–46): *Gross asymmetries in income distribution matter to people. To start with, they are a sign of social injustice... we inhabit a planet where, as an aggregate, the wealthiest quintile of the population enjoys more than 70 per cent of total income compared to a meagre two per cent for the poorest quintile (83 versus 1 per cent under market exchange rates). We also live in a world where more than eight million young children die each year (some 22,000 per day), and most of their deaths are preventable. Hunger, malnutrition and lack of safe drinking water contribute to at least half of child mortality, and the incidence is highly concentrated among the poorest quintile... But inequality also matters to economic growth... Inequality is economically inefficient and dysfunctional... consumption is concentrated in the top income quintile in most developing countries, making their markets smaller... Last but not least, inequality matters to political stability. Gross inequalities tend to generate intense social tensions and even violent conflict.*

2. The Committee for the Compilation of Materials on Damage Caused by the Atomic Bombs in Hiroshima and Nagasaki (1981). *Hiroshima and Nagasaki: The Physical, Medical, and Social Effects of the Atomic Bombings.* New York, Basic Books.

3. Gibson, David R. (2012). *Talk at the Brink: Deliberation and Decision during the Cuban Missile Crisis.* Princeton, NJ, Princeton University Press.

4. The Campaign for Nuclear Disarmament (March 2014) publication *People not Trident* provides a range of arguments used by those opposed to continued reliance and expenditure on a nuclear deterrent.

5. McKibben, Bill (2011). *The Global Warming Reader.* OR Books.

6. Bunyan, John (1678/2008). *The Pilgrim's Progress.* Penguin Classics. The reference is to the Celestial City, the destination of Christian's journey in search of salvation.

7. Keen, M. H. (1973). *England in the Later Middle Ages.* Methuen. The words are those of John Ball, a radical Christian preacher, who met his death in the Great Peasants' Revolt of 1381 in England during the reign of Richard II (see p. 266–271). The democratic state set up during a civil war is a reference to the Diggers community set up on St George's Hill near London during the English Civil War in 1649 – see Hill, Christopher (1961): *The Century of Revolution 1603–1714* (Nelson).

8. The Christian religion offers a promise of salvation for souls after death in a heaven where all are equal before God, their creator.

9. In the United Kingdom (UK), the voting age was lowered to eighteen in 1969; this is the same in most countries in the world and all countries in Europe.

10. Winters, Jeffrey A. (2011). *Oligarchy*. Cambridge University Press.

11. A seminal definition expressed in 1863 by Abraham Lincoln, the President of the United States of America. The USA is still the wealthiest and most powerful of the developed countries and a neighbour, although separated by an ocean, to the land, England, where Pilgrim journeys.

12. Stiglitz, Joseph E. (2011). *Of the 1%, by the 1%, for the 1%*. V*anity Fair,* May edition.

13. Chomsky, Noam. Extracts from a speech delivered by Chomsky in Bonn, Germany at DW Global Media Forum, 15th August 2013.

14. Schimank, Uwe and Volkmann, Ute (ed.) (2012). *The Marketization of Society: Economizing the Non-Economic*. Bremen.

15. Krugman, Paul (2012). *End this Depression Now!* W. W. Norton & Co; Chang, Ha-Joon (2010) *23 Things They Don't Tell You About Capitalism*. Penguin Books.

16. 'Mammon' is a term used to describe gluttony and unjust worldly gain in the Christian Bible. It was first personified as a false god in the New Testament of that Bible. (Mt. 6.24; Lk. 16.13.)

17. The Interpreter's references to *a land thousands of miles away... to the east* seem in the context to indicate the former Soviet Union, and specifically, at the time of Pilgrim's journey, the country known as Russia. The president of Russia is Vladimir Putin; his power

appears to be orchestrated in part by Vladislav Surkov, the vice-head of the presidential administration. (See Pomerantsev, Peter, *Putin's Rasputin. London Review of Books*, 20th October 2011.)

18. The fastest and most famous of all the Gilbert and Sullivan patter songs, *I Am the Very Model of a Modern Major-General*, is also one of the most parodied. See Bradley, Ian (1982), *The Annotated Gilbert and Sullivan 1*, p. 114–117, Penguin.) It would seem an apt choice for a specialist in postmodernist deception and self-parody.

19. No Benefit's speech to Pilgrim here is almost identical to sections of an article written by a minister, Iain Duncan Smith, in the United Kingdom (UK) coalition government 2010–2015 entitled *I don't apologise for trying to make the welfare state fair – it's something only this government can do* (*The Guardian*, Monday 29th July 2013).

20. Surveillance by the state of individual citizens has increased exponentially on the back of the digital revolution. The National Security Agency (NSA) in the USA, along with similar signals intelligence agencies in the UK, Canada, Australia and New Zealand, has for the last half-century and more sought to monitor as many of the world's communications as is technically possible. On a planet of seven billion people and nearly the same number of mobile phones, with six billion emails sent every hour, the NSA claims to 'touch' 1.6% of global Internet traffic and puts no ceiling on its interception aspirations. (Soar, Daniel, *How to get ahead at the NSA. London Review of Books*, 24th October 2013.)

21. The history of economics as an academic discipline has been described as "an epistemological scandal of immense proportions" by Manfred Max Neef and Philip B. Smith in Kalle Lasn (2012), *Meme Wars: The Creative Destruction of Neo-Classical Economics*. Penguin.

22. The Interpreter's explanation is similar to that provided by John Lanchester, *Let's call it failure*, *London Review of Books*, 3rd January 2013.

23. Ross McKibben (*London Review of Books*, 25th April 2013) in his article *Anything but Benevolent* points out that *The differences between what people think about the welfare state and its reality are very striking. They believe that 41 per cent of the welfare budget is spent on the unemployed: the figure is actually 3 per cent. They believe that 27 per cent of the welfare budget is claimed fraudulently: the government estimates it is 0.7 per cent.*

24. The democratically elected mayor, Boris Johnson, of Pilgrim's island's capital city, London, is reported as making a speech in which similar sentiments were expressed, during the period of Pilgrim's truth-searching journey. He was heard to say that "greed" and "the spirit of envy" are "a valuable spur to economic activity" and "It is surely relevant to a conversation about equality that as many as 16% of our species have an IQ below 85, while about 2% have an IQ above 130." (See an article, written very shortly after the speech, by Andrew Rawnsley in *The Observer*, December 1st 2013.) Boris Johnson and the Prime Minister (David Cameron) and Chancellor of the Exchequer (George Osborne) of the United Kingdom's government at this time all shared similar backgrounds, enjoying wealth,

privilege and an elite education that actually brought them into the membership of the same dining club, the Bullingdon Society, at university in Oxford.

25. The story of the Good Samaritan in the Christian Bible (Lk 10: 25–37) is a seminal text for beginning to understand the startlingly original view of the mendicant Jewish carpenter, Jesus of Nazareth, that 'enemies', the ones who are disliked, scapegoated and seen as different and inferior, are worthy of our love too. This carpenter from Nazareth, the founder of the Christian religion (see above, Reference 8), is believed to have lived some two thousand years ago and spread numerous such subversive messages over a three-year period before being crucified to death by the Roman authorities on the recommendation of the religious leaders of his own people.

26. In the UK, a Health and Social Care Act was passed in March 2012, authorising the reorganisation of the National Health Service. It encouraged competition as a key tool for improving quality, increasing productivity, driving down costs and widening choice for patients. The cost of such reorganisation has been calculated at £3 billion. Clinical commissioning groups replaced primary care trusts in order to maximise this competition, and 49% of hospital services were now opened up to the private sector. It is predicted that the private sector health market will be worth £200 billion by 2030. Between 2010 and 2013, it has been calculated that the private sector acquired £7 billion of business from the NHS and a new legal industry was created around competition and procurement of services. (*The*

Observer editorial, 10th November 2013; Toynbee, Polly, *They're calling it a health revolution*, *The Guardian*, 2nd April 2013.)

27. The National Health Service had been established in the UK in 1948 under the socialist Labour government (1945–51), elected in a landslide victory after the end of World War 2, a war fought successfully against Nazi-controlled Germany, a right-wing dictatorship at that time, and its allies.

28. Public satisfaction with the National Health Service, according to surveys, peaked in 2010 before the new government took power. It then plummeted as news of reorganisation (and scandals) became dominant. (Toynbee, Polly, *Integration? The Guardian*, 11th October 2012.)

29. A series of scandals within the National Health Service began to be revealed in the early years of the 21st century as a result of whistleblowing, investigative journalism and statistical analysis within the field of medicine. As a result legal enquiries were set up, for instance to investigate abnormally high mortality rates in mid-Staffordshire and high infant mortality at Morecambe Bay. Issues in front-line nursing also received attention; in Liverpool, it was established that a putative 'care pathway' had led to nurses shouting at visitors not to give dying relatives a sip of water for fear it might affect the hospital's recording of targets. (Jenkins, Simon, *Another NHS crisis? The Guardian*, 17th July 2013.) Target-setting may be seen as yet another illustration of the mania for measurement; the product of insecure times (see above, p. 64).

30. Naomi Klein made the argument in *The Shock Doctrine: The Rise of Disaster Capitalism* (2007, Allen Lane: Penguin Books) that every crisis is an opportunity to impose what she terms 'disaster capitalism' on those affected. John Harris, writing in *The Guardian* (28th February 2011), cites one of the leading exponents of an unregulated market, the economist Milton Friedman: *Only a crisis – actual or perceived – produces real change. When that crisis occurs the actions that are taken depend on the ideas that are lying around. That, I believe, is our basic function: to develop alternatives to existing policies, to keep them alive and available until the politically impossible becomes politically inevitable.* Harris sets out the case that the UK government (2010–15) used the crisis of laissez-faire capitalism that had nearly brought bankruptcy to the banking system in 2008 as an opportunity to attack the benefit system and market the NHS, the education system, and the entire public sector. He points out the irony that a crisis of unregulated capitalism is begetting more unregulated capitalism.

31. The new Prime Minister of the Labour government (1945–51), Clement Attlee, and the health and housing minister, Aneurin (Nye) Bevan, led a systematic and ideologically inspired effort to rebuild a war-damaged economy and nation through a massive programme of nationalisation, none of which survives today apart from the National Health Service. In 2013, a film documentary, *The Spirit of '45*, was released. Directed by Ken Loach, it used archive material of the men and women whose lives were affected by these changes to illustrate how an effective democracy could gain the ascendancy over

oligarchy and plutocracy, at least in some measure and for a limited period of time.

32. The manifesto of the Labour party in the 1945 general election had included Clause IV, which promised *to secure for the workers by hand or brain the full fruits of their industry... upon the basis of the common ownership of the means of production, distribution and exchange.* The manifesto also promised a housing programme to ensure that *every family has a good standard of accommodation.* In 1994, the Labour party agreed, at its annual conference, to abandon the wording of Clause IV and adopted the term 'New Labour' as a party slogan. From 1994–2010, 'New Labour' was presented as the brand of a party that had found a new way between capitalism and socialism, which endorsed market economics within a framework of social justice.

33. The Interpreter's account is supported by the oral testimony of those affected in Loach's documentary film (see above, Reference 31).

34. Mark Twain, the American author and humourist, popularised the saying in *Chapters from My Autobiography*, published in the *North American Review* in 1906. The earliest instance of a version of the saying found in print dates to a letter published in 1891 in *The National Observer* in London: *Sir... It has been wittily remarked that there are three kinds of falsehood: the first is a 'fib', the second is a downright lie, and the third and the most aggravated is statistics.* (13th June 1891.)

35. In 1998, one of the founders of the New Labour party, Peter Mandelson, expressed the view that he was "intensely relaxed about people getting filthy rich". He

did so as a cabinet minister in the context of looking forward to silicon valley-like IT development in the UK, and he hurriedly added, "As long as they pay their taxes" to his comment. John Rentoul in *The Independent* (14th February 2013) reported that the comments were first recorded by David Wighton in the *Financial Times* (23rd October 1998) and then by Victor Keegan in *The Guardian* (26th October 1998).

36. Jenny Kitzinger reported: *Focus groups are a form of group interview that capitalises on communication between research participants in order to generate data... [they] can be used to examine not only what people think but how they think and why they think that way* (*British Medical Journal*, 1995; 311.299). From the 1950s to the 1980s, the focus group became a structural part of marketing, before being absorbed into politics. Jules Peck and Robert Phillips concluded that politics in the United States of America under the presidency of Bill Clinton (1993–2001) became centred on the wishes of swing voters in response to the adoption of the focus group at the heart of policy-making. Political leadership, required to deal with pressing national and international issues, was diverted by this concern to win votes. (*Citizen Renaissance*, Chapter 5. Internet, 2009–11.)

37. In 2005, the European Court of Human Rights ruled that the UK ban on prisoners having the right to vote needed amendment. In 2010, David Cameron, the UK Prime Minister (2010–present) said it made him "physically ill" to contemplate giving any convicted prisoners the vote. A parliamentary committee is at

present considering the UK government's draft bill on prisoners' voting eligibility. In 2013, the UK Attorney General, Dominic Grieve, warned of "a degree of anarchy" as a consequence of what had now become an eight-year period of defiance of European legislation (Joshua Rozenberg; Alan Travis, *The Guardian*, Wednesday 6th November 2013.)

38. Tom Clark and Rowena Mason. *Poll reveals anger, not boredom, lies behind drop in political engagement. The Guardian*, Thursday 26th November 2013.

39. Toynbee, Polly. *We must all share the blame for our 'useless' politicians. The Guardian*, Monday 30th December 2013. Polly Toynbee singled out David Cameron, the Prime Minister, for his mendacity. She cites, among others, the following examples: *Nick Clegg [then the Deputy Prime Minister] gets most blame over [promising no] tuition fees, a promise that won university seats and then betrayed so many fresh first-time voters. But David Cameron wins the mendacity prize by what he might call a country mile. He pledged no rise in VAT [value added tax]; it rose immediately. On child benefit the Prime Minister said, "I wouldn't means test it", but he did. The education maintenance allowance would stay; it went. Vote blue [Conservative], go green [a party slogan] became "get rid of all the green crap" [a remark alleged to have been made by the Prime Minister earlier in 2013].*

40. Bryan Gould. *Voters disenchanted with democracy can be cured. The Guardian*. Monday 6th January 2014.

41. There was a coordinated day of anti-war protests across the world on 15th February 2003 as people in more than six hundred cities expressed opposition to the

imminent invasion of Iraq by an alliance of governments led by the USA under the presidency of George W. Bush (2001–2009) with the close support of the UK under the premiership of Tony Blair (1997–2007). At least one million people demonstrated against the war in London; three million in Rome. According to Bush and Blair, the invasion (which nevertheless began on 19th March 2003, despite the demonstrations) was necessary in order to disarm Iraq of weapons of mass destruction, to end Iraqi support for terrorism, and to free the Iraqi people from the dictatorship of their leader, Saddam Hussein. (BBC News Online, 17–19th February 2003.) As it turned out, the weapons of mass destruction did not exist and the support for terrorism was difficult to substantiate; Saddam Hussein was removed from power and judicially executed. Iraq is now a state riven by violence fuelled by sectarian differences.

42. The United Kingdom parliamentary expenses scandal in 2009 aroused widespread anger among the public against MPs, and a loss of confidence in the political system. It arose following publication by the *Telegraph* group of leaked details of the misuse of expense claims made by members of the House of Commons and House of Lords over several years. It led to a large number of resignations, sackings, deselections and retirement announcements, together with public apologies and the repayment of expenses. Several politicians were prosecuted and sentenced to terms of imprisonment. (*The Daily Telegraph*, 5th February 2010; Martin, Ian, *How the Rotten Parliament (2005–10) Sold Our Birthright. The Wall Street Journal*, 6th February 2010.)

43. The Headmaster's aspirations are similar to those of Michael Gove, the minister for education in the UK coalition government (2010–15). A flavour of the criticism of such ideas and policies can be found in Jenkins, Simon, *Napoleon Gove can dictate its terms but the school curriculum is bogus. The Guardian*, 26th November 2010; Moore, Suzanne, *Michael Gove's fundamentalist meddling is about conforming to a dimly imagined past. The Guardian*, 13th June 2013 and Rosen, Michael, *Dear Mr Gove: [a] letter from a curious parent. The Guardian*, 1st October 2013. Michael Rosen concluded: *Your [Michael Gove's] legacy is the near-complete destruction of local democratic running of schools. You adopt a rhetoric... that dresses this up in the language of liberty... but then forget to tell us that this new freedom is controlled by a political interference from... one person – the education secretary [Michael Gove].*

44. The UK general election in May 2010 saw the Conservative party gain 306 seats, insufficient to form a majority government as the Labour party had secured 258 seats and the Liberal Democrat party fifty-seven seats. A coalition government was formed between the Conservatives and the Liberal Democrats. Thirty-six per cent of the electorate (10.7 million voters) had opted for the Conservatives; 29% (8.6 million) for the Labour party; and 23% (6.8 million) for the Liberal Democrats. (Electoral Commission website, retrieved 25th January 2014.)

45. BBC News, 18th May 2013. *Michael Gove heckled at head teacher's conference in Birmingham* (http://www.

bbc.co./news/education-22558756). Retrieved 27th October 2013.

46. Ryan, Chris and Sibieta, Luke. *Private Schooling in the UK and Australia* (http://www.ifs.org.uk/bns/bn106. pdf). Institute of Fiscal Studies, 2010.

47. Herbert Marcuse (1898–1979) was a radical American academic whose work *One Dimensional Man: The Ideology of Industrial Society* (1964) was hailed at the time as the most subversive book published in the United States that century. (See Abromeit, John and Mark Cobb, W., eds. (2004), *Herbert Marcuse: A Critical Reader.* New York, London: Routledge.)

48. Marcuse wrote in his conclusion to *One Dimensional Man* that *Nothing indicates that it will be a good end. The economic and technical capabilities of the established societies are sufficiently vast to allow for adjustments and concessions to the under-dog, and their armed forces sufficiently trained and equipped to take care of emergency situations.* He does, however, allow the thin glimmer of hope, quoting Walter Benjamin in translation: *It is only for the sake of those without hope that hope is given to us* (p. 201, First Sphere Books edition, 1968).

49. The issue of 'repressive desublimation' is analysed in Chapter 3 of the first section, *One-Dimensional Society* in Marcuse (1964), p. 58–76.

50. Ignorance is a character in Bunyan's *The Pilgrim's Progress* (1678) who follows a different path to the Celestial City. Pilgrim's encounters with Ignorance leave no doubt that Ignorance has the wrong theology. The penultimate sentence of the work has Ignorance, bound hand and foot, carried through the air to the

door in the side of the hill by the Gates of Heaven that leads to Hell – and put inside. (p.164)

51. See above, p. 40–42.

52. George Akerlof in Lasn (2012), *Meme Wars*, draws attention to Keynes' words. Akerlof makes the case that economists have to start adding norms and motivations back into their models. Lasn (2012) has no page numbers; it is not a conventional work.

53. In Lasn (2012), the economic arguments against growth are outlined by, inter alia: Herman Daly in his idea of a steady state economy (SSE); Ted Trainer in his exploration of the profoundly radical implications of zero growth; Bernard Stiegler in his rejection of the consumerist model; Brian Davey in his analysis of attempts in Ecuador and Bolivia to create what he terms the Good Life in a post-growth economy; and Tarek El Diwany in his assessment of Islamic economics based on interest-free markets.

54. Steve Keen in Lasn (2012) presents a study of this battle within universities for the soul of economics as an academic discipline. He acknowledges that *although there are multiple schools of thought extant – from Post Keynesian to Evolutionary and Behavioral Economics, and Econophysics – these are not developed enough to provide a fully-fledged alternative to neoclassical economics*. He still insists that *This should not dissuade us from dispensing completely with the neoclassical approach.*

55. Charles Darwin published *The Origin of Species* in 1859 in which he provided his evidence for his theory of evolution. Within a generation, the theory had gained

acceptance within the scientific community as the most plausible explanation for the diversity of life. It retains that status for nearly all academics and many people today. (See Coyne, Jerry A. 2009. *Why Evolution is True.* Oxford: Oxford University Press.)

56. The Occupy movement was an international protest movement against global market forces and growing inequalities. It began in New York on Wall Street in September 2011 and spread across urban centres in the United States and the rest of the democratic world in the period 2011–12.

57. Slovak Žižek is a Slovenian-born Marxist philosopher born in 1949. He holds academic posts in both Slovenia and London. Further insight is provided in Wood, Kelsey (2012). *Žižek: A Reader's Guide.* Wiley-Blackwell.

58. Roberto Mangabeira Unger is an Argentinian-born philosopher, social theorist and politician born in 1947. He is at present Professor of Law at Harvard Law School in the USA. A recent expression of his political thought is in Unger, Roberto (2009), *The Left Alternative*, Verso (2nd edition to *What Should the Left Propose?*, Verso, 2006).

59. Between 2007 and 2009 Unger served as a government minister in Brazil, attempting to implement policies that widened economic and educational opportunities. His development strategy for the Amazon rainforest region favoured the interests of local people against those who sought to exploit them and their land.

60. See above, p. 82 and Reference 56. Also see Byrne, Janet (editor, 2012), *The Occupy Handbook*, Back Bay Books and Runciman, David, *Stiffed*, *London Review of Books*, 25th October 2012. Runciman, in his essay, reviewed

Byrne's work and concluded that *the victims who need the most help are [the young people; the 5%] who are struggling to stay afloat in the labour market.* This is a theme that the Interpreter himself embraces as he further explains the duties of democratic government to Pilgrim (see p. 86–89).

61. Between 6th and 11th August 2011, thousands of people rioted in several London boroughs and in a number of cities and towns across England, resulting in five deaths and over three thousand arrests. See Phillips, Richard; Frost, Diane and Singleton, Alex (March 2013). *Researching the Riots. The Geographical Journal*, Vol. 179, No. 1.

62. The case for a more forthright parliamentary opposition is made, for instance, by Jonathan Freedland in *This summer Labour cannot rest – or it may lose the battle, The Guardian*, 19th July 2013, and by John Harris in *The average Briton can't imagine Ed Miliband in Downing Street, according to the polls, The Guardian*, 12th August 2013. A counter-argument is presented by Polly Toynbee in *Ed Miliband spent the past year laying building blocks for his policies, The Guardian*, 16th August 2013.

63. In September 2010, Ed Miliband was elected the new leader of the Labour party, now in opposition after the May 2010 general election. The Interpreter, in an earlier discussion with Pilgrim, remarked on the importance of the measurement and manipulation of public opinion in contemporary politics (see p. 64–66). It seems that the Interpreter here believes that the leader of the opposition is too cautious and has, in effect, acted on political calculation rather than a principled

determination to expose a government that acts in the interests of the wealthy and powerful few.

64. See above, Reference 32.

65. The Interpreter's historical analysis of the contemporary housing crisis in the United Kingdom is similar to that presented by James Meek in *Where will we live? London Review of Books*, 9th January 2014.

66. James Meek (2014) cites David Orr's prescription (he is the head of the National Housing Federation, the umbrella body for housing associations): *Right now we spend £10.5 billion per annum on housing and transport* – £9.5 billion on transport, and £1 billion on housing. If we decided *[to spend £1 billion less on transport and £1 billion more on housing], we would be building forty thousand new homes a year.*

67. See above, p. 5

68. The Butler Education Act of 1944 made all schooling, including secondary, free for all pupils and raised the school leaving age to fifteen. The tripartite division the Interpreter refers to in fact became a bipartite division between grammar and secondary modern schools; few technical schools were established. (See Simon, Brian, *The 1944 Education Act: A Conservative Measure? History of Education*, 1986.)

69. See above, p. 76–77.

70. The so-called nature-nurture argument is examined in Goldhaber, Dale (2012). *The Nature-Nurture Debates: Bridging the Gap*. Cambridge University Press.

71. Within the disciplines of psychology and sociology, the Pygmalion effect refers to the phenomenon in which the greater the expectation placed upon people, the better

they perform. Conversely, the golem effect refers to low expectations leading to a decrease in performance. Both effects are forms of self-fulfilling prophecy. Rosenthal and Jacobson (1968) discussed the Pygmalion effect in the classroom at length and concluded that if teachers were led to expect enhanced performance from some children, then the children did demonstrate that improvement. (Rosenthal, Robert and Jacobson, Lenore (1968/1992). *Pygmalion in the classroom*, expanded ed. New York: Irvington.) The Pygmalion hypotheses are also supported by Brophy, Jere E. and Good, Thomas L. *Teachers' communication of differential expectations for children's classroom performance; some behavioural data. Journal of Educational Psychology*, Vol. 61 (5), October 1970.

72. The comprehensive school idea – children of all backgrounds and abilities being taught together in the same school – can be traced back to the 1920s but the decisive moment came in 1964 with the election of a Labour government committed to their introduction. Between 1965 and 1975, virtually all state secondary schools in Wales and Scotland went comprehensive; in England the figure was about 90%. This transformation took place under both Labour and Conservative governments, with the pace of change being even quicker under the Conservatives. (Pring, Richard and Walford, Geoffrey. *Comprehensive schools: the history. The Times Higher Education*, 15th January 1996.)

73. John Ermisch, acknowledging the inherent methodological problems in such research, concluded nevertheless that divorce in the UK reduces the

chances that children obtain higher qualifications. (John Ermisch, *Effects on divorce on children*. Institute of Social and Economic Research, University of Essex, 2009.)

74. Several events stand out in the last forty or so years as markers for what the Interpreter identifies as a political agenda intent on establishing that schools were not good enough. The Labour Prime Minister James Callaghan made a speech at Ruskin College, Oxford in 1976 that was designed to initiate a "great debate" about education in order to raise standards to compete more effectively in the highly competitive world of international industry and commerce. Under the premiership of Margaret Thatcher, the Conservative government reorganised the schools inspectorate and instituted OFSTED (now the Office for Standards in Education, Children's Services and Skills) in 1984. Every state school now faced regular inspection and a public report, on the basis of common criteria that applied to all inspections. In 1988, the National Curriculum was introduced under the terms of the Education Reform Act of that year. The content of what was taught in schools was now standardised across the land, enabling assessment of outcomes to be measured and league tables to be compiled to rank schools according to performance. See Jones, Ken (2003). *Education in Britain: 1944 to the Present*. Blackwell: Oxford. Interestingly, the European country with the most impressive record of children's educational achievement is Finland, which has no national inspection framework and lacks a rigid national curriculum (Abrams, Samuel E. *The Children*

Must Play: What We Can Learn From Educational Reform in Finland. The New Republic, January 2011).

75. Ha-Joon Chang (2010) in *23 Things They Don't Tell You About Capitalism* (Allen Lane: Penguin) argues against the idea that more education is in itself going to make a country richer (p. 178–189). *What really matters in the determination of national prosperity is not the educational levels of individuals but the nation's ability to organise individuals into enterprises with higher productivity* (p.179); *Education is valuable [because it helps] us develop our potentials and live a more fulfilling and independent life* (p.189).

76. In 1997, the Dearing Report had recommended that students should contribute to the costs of their university education. The Labour government, under the premiership of Tony Blair, passed the Teaching and Higher Education Act of 1998, which introduced tuition fees, initially set at £1,000 per annum. The Higher Education Act of 2004 increased tuition fees to a maximum of £3,000 per year.

77. Paton, Graeme. *Cost of a degree 'to rise to £26,000' after tuition fee hike. The Daily Telegraph*, 11th July 2013.

78. Gypsies have a long history as persecuted outsiders and some media are quick to highlight any links with criminality – see, for instance, Mail Online, Tuesday 11th March 2014, in which Jack Doyle cites a HM Prisons Inspectorate report that about 5% of the prison population (4,300 prisoners) self-identify as gypsies, Roma or travellers. Roma gypsies are a particular ethnic group that have occasionally made the headlines in the United Kingdom in the first half

of the second decade of this century, not least because of the similarity of the word 'Roma' with the term 'Romanian', describing a citizen of Romania, an Eastern European country that recently became a member of the European Community, and from January 2013 enjoyed migration rights across the community. Opinion polls in the United Kingdom show that the fear of uncontrolled immigration is very powerful. Griff Witte in *The Washington Post*, 7th January 2014, reported that opinion polls (in *Transatlantic Trends: Key Findings, 2013*) show that Britons have significantly more negative views about immigrants than either their fellow Europeans or Americans. A nationalist party, the United Kingdom Independence Party (UKIP), has developed a large following and poses a significant electoral threat to the ruling Conservative party. Anger about 'immigrants taking our job and our benefits' may have as much electoral sway as any concerns about inequality and the unfair distribution of wealth in the absence of an articulate opposition party, prepared to explain what is happening in the government of the country.

79. David Cameron left the world of the Conservative party briefly in 1994 to become the Director of Corporate Affairs at Carlton Communications, a growing media company (see Robinson, James; Teather, David, *Cameron – the PR years. The Guardian*, 20th February 2010).

80. Glen Owen reported in *The Mail on Sunday*, 23rd May 2010, that twenty-three of the twenty-nine members of the new cabinet were millionaires and the Lib Dems

in the coalition government were just as wealthy as the Tories. Andrew Grice in *The Independent*, 8th November 2013, noted that Jeremy Hunt, the Secretary of State for Health, was set to become the richest member of the cabinet after the sale of his own company for a £17 million profit. Other cabinet millionaires include Philip Hammond (£8.2m), William Hague (£4.8m), George Osborne (£4.5m), David Cameron (£3.8m), Francis Maude (£3.2m) and Dominic Grieve (£2.9m).

81. Wikipedia is a collaboratively edited, multilingual, free Internet encyclopaedia that is supported by the non-profit Wikimedia Foundation. Jimmy Wales and Larry Sanger launched Wikipedia in 2001 – 'wiki' deriving from the Hawaiian for 'quick'.

82. The BBC television programme *Newsnight* reported on 2nd March 2007 that such a photograph had been withdrawn for 'commercial reasons' by the photographers, who added that they had had no contact with the Conservative party.

83. See above, p. 28–30.

84. The corrupting nature of power was captured by Lord Acton (1834–1902) in a letter to Bishop Mandell Creighton, 3rd April 1887 (see *Life and Letters of Mandell Creighton*, 1904, i. 372).

85. Winston Churchill (1874–1965) expressed these views about democracy in a speech in the House of Commons on 11th November 1947 as leader of the opposition.

86. John Rawls (1921–2002) produced his seminal work in political philosophy, *A Theory of Justice*, in 1971. See Wolff, Jonathan (1996). *An Introduction to Political Philosophy*. Oxford University Press.

87. Cohen, Nick. *Cowardly coalition can't face fact of food banks. The Observer*, 29th December 2013.

88. Butler, Patrick. *Demand for food banks 'fuelled by poverty and benefit delays'. The Guardian*, 20th February 2014.

89. Gibbon, Garry. *Work Programme needs more work.* Channel 4 News blog, 12th March 2014.

90. *The Selfish Capitalist* (2008) is the title of a work by Oliver James, a psychologist, in which he argues that the English-speaking world has been hijacked by Selfish Capitalism for the last thirty years. There has been a marked increase in emotional distress as a consequence.

91. Elliot, Larry. *Another year in which earnings rise less than prices could hit the recovery and David Cameron's re-election hopes. The Guardian*, 30th December 2013; Keegan, William. *You don't need to be Einstein to see why Osborne was wrong. The Observer*, 23rd March 2014.

92. Kettle, Martin. *Growth doesn't guarantee a Tory victory. The Guardian*, 30th January 2014.

93. *The Observer*, 30th March 2014, p. 1 and p. 6.

94. Monaghan, Angela. *UK austerity measures likely to hurt society's poorest, OECD warns. The Guardian*, 19th March 2014.

95. Elliott, Larry. *Oxfam report reveals scale of inequality in UK. The Guardian*, 17th March 2014.

96. Larry Elliott wrote *If the opinion polls are right, Britain will wake up politically rudderless on Friday* in his article *Deficit, deceit, deals and delusion...* (*The Guardian*, 4th May 2015.) He went on to argue that the chancellor, George Osborne, *has not presided over an economic miracle and appears to have learned nothing from the experience of the last parliament... trying to cut*

borrowing too fast will lead to slower growth and slower progress on deficit reduction.

97. An almost immediate analysis by Alberto Nardelli concluded *The party viewed as better at managing the economy, and the one with the more competent leader (according to the British public) won the election.* A substantial number of previous Labour voters had simply opted to vote for the Tories. In constituencies in the Midlands – such as High Peak, Amber Valley and Nuneaton – middle-class families concerned about the economy chose the Tories over Labour. The Tories beat Labour in suburban constituencies, including in London's outer boroughs. *In the end, the polls were right in Scotland. They weren't in England.* (Nardelli, Alberto. *Tory Triumph a bolt from the blue. How did the polls get it so wrong? The Guardian,* 9th May 2015.)

98. In an online article, Bart Cammaerts, an associate professor at the London School of Economics, noted that in the 2015 campaign all the daily newspapers, bar *The Guardian* and the leftist tabloid *The Daily Mirror,* were extremely pro-Tory and anti-Labour. The explanation, he claimed, was relatively simple. Almost all the newspapers in the UK are the personal property of billionaires: the Australian media tycoon Rupert Murdoch owns *The Sun* and *The Times,* Viscount Rothermere *The Daily Mail,* the Barclay brothers *The Daily Telegraph* and the Russian oligarch Lebedev *The Independent* and *The Evening Standard.* Together these men are worth £12 billion. Their interest would be better served by a right-wing party in power, not least because the Labour party manifesto suggested

they wanted to implement the recommendations in Lord Leveson's report concerning press ethics and the lack of pluralism in the British newspaper industry. (Cammaerts, Bart, 2015. *Did Britain's right-wing newspapers win the election for the Tories?* (http://blogs. lse.ac.uk/politicsandpolicy/did-britains-right-wing-newspapers-win-the el... 02/09/2015)

99. William Keegan wrote: *...it cannot be repeated often enough [that the financial crash] was not caused by the public spending of which Cameron and Osborne approved at the time, but by a banking "system" that had spun completely out of control.* (Keegan, William. *As Osborne cuts, Labour must not suffer a great depression. The Observer*, 28th June 2015.) Dr Anush Kapadia noted in a *Guardian* letter: *What is surprising is the utter lack of robust counter-narrative, especially when there is an almost blindingly obvious response to the charge of New Labour economic mismanagement and excessive borrowing: just ask the bond markets.* Kapadia's point is that UK government ten-year gilts remained relatively stable over the entire period of New Labour rule. The UK was no Greece – it kept the confidence of the markets. (Kapadia, Anush. *The Guardian* letters page. 26th June 2015.)

100. Jonathan Freedland gave his own participant account of the refusal of the Labour leadership to address the past and refute the Conservative claims: *I have some sympathy for those Labour operatives now insisting they urged Miliband to confront the Tory/Lib Dem narrative of Labour fiscal incompetence, only to be rebuffed – because I experienced that rebuffing for myself. In conversation*

during the leadership campaign in the summer of 2010, I asked Miliband how he would counter the new coalition's repeated claim that they were merely "cleaning up the mess left by Labour". Surely Labour had to confront that claim soon, before it hardened into accepted fact... Miliband was unmoved. "I just think what we say about the future matters more." (Freedland, Jonathan. 'Moving on': the mantra that traps politicians in the past. *The Guardian*, 6th June 2015.)

101. Larry Elliot summarised these failings in the article cited above: Reference 96. In relation to the issue of an over-stimulated housing market, Larry Elliot later wrote that George Osborne's strategy of heating up the property market from 2012 in order to get a sluggish economy going and claim a recovery now meant another boom-bust was on the cards. (Elliot, Larry. *Brewing housing storm could sink economy. The Guardian*, 5th October 2015.)

102. Matthew Francis, Teaching Fellow at the University of Birmingham, pointed out in a pre-election online article the long-running nature of the Conservative strategy to undermine the economic credibility of the Labour party. He concluded that the arguments would be unlikely to survive the scrutiny of professional economists but they did translate complex ideas into easy-to-understand examples. (Francis, Matthew, 2015. *Tory attacks on Labour's 'economic chaos' stretch back to this cartoon from the 1930s.* http://theconversation. com/tory-attacks-on-labours-economic-chaos-stretch-back-to-the Retrieved 2nd September 2015.) Bart Cammaerts (2015) – cited above, Reference 98 – argued

that *it is clear that the UK media did set a certain tone, they outlined the contours of public debate and they have had an influence on how and on what people think.* However, he also sounds a note of academic caution. *We must also recognise that what drives people to vote for or against a particular party is complex and cannot be merely reduced to their media consumption.*

103. The referendum on independence for Scotland was held on 18th September 2014 with the No vote (55.3%) defeating the Yes vote (44.7%). The turnout was a phenomenal 84.6%, in sharp contrast to the early 21st century general election figures of 50–60%. The nation had become politically energised.

104. Nicola Sturgeon MSP, the leader of the Scottish National Party (SNP), had impressed all parties in the televised leaders' debates before the UK general election in 2015. (https://en.wikipedia.org/wiki/Nicola_Sturgeon)   The SNP opposition to austerity was in sharp contrast to the so-called 'austerity-lite' approach of the Labour Party. SNP website, *SNP will increase spending and end Tory austerity.* Retrieved 23rd April 2015.

105. Support for the Scottish National Party in opinion polls greatly increased in the weeks following the referendum. In the 2015 general election on 7th May, the SNP came third across the whole of the UK, in terms of Westminster seats won. The SNP received nearly 1.5 million votes, 50% of the Scottish votes, winning fifty-six out of the fifty-nine seats. Scottish Labour lost forty out of their forty-one sitting MPs. (*Election 2015: SNP wins 56 of 59 seats in Scots landslide.* BBC News, 8th May 2015. Retrieved 20th June 2015.)

106. These attacks became even more systematic during the general election campaign in 2015. Conservative candidates had been instructed to put attacks on Ed Miliband at the heart of their campaigns in a briefing message reportedly seen by Sky News. Focus points outlined in the dossier include: *Ed Miliband just isn't up to the job of Prime Minister – he's weak and short-termist* and *Expect the chaos and uncertainty of a weak Prime Minister* and *The Labour Party under Miliband has repeatedly refused to rule out a coalition with the SNP.* (http://news.sky.com/story/1461837/tory-dossier-urges-attacks-on-ed-miliband. Retrieved 9th April 2015.)

107. Andrew Rawnsley noted in September 2014 that pollsters were being told *two particularly wounding and personal things about Mr Miliband: few of them think that he is up to being Prime Minister and few of them think that he is capable of taking tough decisions.* (Rawnsley, Andrew, *The Observer.* 28th September 2014.)

108. Ed Miliband resigned as leader immediately after his defeat on 7th May 2015. The closing date for nominations in the ensuing leadership election was 15th June. A backbench MP with a reputation for party rebellion, Jeremy Corbyn, was nominated at the very last minute by the required number of MPs as, in effect, the token socialist candidate. If Corbyn was Lizzie's 'breath of hope', he remained the bookies' 200–1 outsider. On 5th July Corbyn began to be seen as a serious contender when the Unite trade union backed him as their candidate. Voting reforms introduced by Ed Miliband meant the unions no longer had block votes, but

their members could vote as affiliated members – and anyone who declared they shared Labour's core values could vote in the leadership election as a supporter if they paid a minimum of £3. (Patrick Wintour, *Labour leadership. The Guardian*, 11th September 2015.)

109. Piketty, Thomas (2014). *Capital in the Twenty-First Century.* Harvard University Press.

110. Will Hutton endorsed Piketty's arguments in his review of *Capital*. (Hutton, Will. *Capitalism simply isn't working and here are the reasons why. The Observer*, 13th April 2014.) Hutton noted that inequality of wealth in Europe and the United States is broadly twice the inequality of income – the top 10% have between 60% and 70% of all wealth but only 25–35% of all income. He concluded that the solutions – a top income tax of up to 80%, effective inheritance tax, proper property taxes and, because the issue is global, a global wealth tax – are currently inconceivable, but agreed with Piketty that the task of economists is to make them more conceivable – and *Capital* did just that.

111. See Reference 105 above.

112. The IMF's report (2014): *Redistribution, Inequality and Growth* is cited by Chris Huhne in his favourable review of Piketty (Huhne, Chris. *The extraordinary success of Thomas Piketty's best-seller shows that progressive ideas are at last winning. The Guardian*, 28th April 2014).

113. Stiglitz, Joseph (2015). *The Great Divide.* Allen Lane.

114. The newspaper interview is with Andrew Anthony. (Anthony, Andrew. Cover story: *The New Review. The Observer*, 24th May 2015.)

115. Ha-Joon Chang (2010), *23 Things They Don't Tell You About Capitalism* (Allen Lane) is cited above in Reference 75. Chang is also clear that state-owned enterprises can be successful. Nearly a year before the 2015 general election, he wrote: *When people realise that the history of capitalism is full of highly successful state enterprises, the rush for ever more privatisation can be halted.* (Ha-Joon Chang. *State-owned enterprises can be successful, as some unlikely global enterprises prove. The Guardian*, 31st July 2014.)

116. Ha-Joon Chang (2015). *Leave aside the tired old mantra – here's what 'pro-business' really means. The Guardian*, 4th March 2015.

117. Dr Ha-Joon Chang and seventy-seven others. *Osborne plan has no basis in economics. The Guardian* letters page, 13th June 2015.

118. See above, p. 105–106.

119. The Labour MP Tom Watson, who later in 2015 was to be elected deputy leader of the Labour party, expressed his concern that phone-hacking was rife at the *News of the World*, the paper owned by Rupert Murdoch, *the most powerful media mogul on the planet.* The same jury that had acquitted Rebekah Brooks had found its then-editor, Andy Coulson, guilty along with three senior news editors. Watson concluded: *For David Cameron to appoint Coulson to Downing Street, bypassing all the usual vetting procedures, casts grave doubt over his judgement... In the end this is a story about power. And Murdoch just got too powerful... But it's politicians that gave Murdoch his power. And I'm sorry to say, I don't see much changing.* (Watson, Tom. *Unless media owners are*

constrained, the British public face yet more scandals and cosy relationships that are corrosive to democracy. The Guardian, 26th June 2015.)

120. Seamus Milne, a *Guardian* columnist, noted that in three months in 2015 Jeremy Corbyn had gone from backbench obscurity to winning the Labour party leadership election with more than a quarter of a million votes, nearly 60% of the total. He and his socialist, anti-austerity message had drawn hundreds of thousands into the Labour Party. But the majority of his own party MPs were opposed to him, along with the political and media establishment. (Milne, Seamus. *The Guardian*, 17th September 2015.)

121. Margaret Thatcher was the Conservative leader and Prime Minister from 1979 to 1990, when she was ousted by an internal party revolt and replaced by John Major as leader and Prime Minister. (Campbell, J. 2011. *Margaret Thatcher Volume Two: The Iron Lady.* Random House.)

122. Joseph Stalin, the Russian communist leader from 1929 to his death in 1953, was portrayed as the Man of Steel. (Archer, Jules, 1974. *Man of Steel, Joseph Stalin.* Bailey and Swinfen.)

123. Ed Vulliamy, a veteran *Observer* reporter, noted that his own liberal, reformist newspaper had responded to Jeremy Corbyn's landslide victory with an editorial foreseeing the inevitable failure at a general election of the mandate on which he won. He felt such a judgement failed to do justice to the spirit of the moral principles of equality, peace and justice that underpin the Corbyn movement. He pointed out that the rest of the media

were hostile to Corbyn. Even the *Guardian* had endorsed a candidate who came *humiliatingly last*. The Tory press barons had *performed to script*. (Vulliamy, Ed, 2015. *Why I take issue with the Observer's stance on Corbyn. The Observer*, 20th September 2015.)

124. Seamus Milne noted that in July 2015 the Greek Prime Minister, Alexis Tsipras, agreed to more austerity as the condition of a further bailout and continued membership of the Eurozone. This despite his party, Syriza, forming the new government in January 2015 with a mandate to oppose austerity. (Milne, Seamus. *The Crucifixion of Greece is killing the European project. The Guardian*, 17th July 2015.)

125. Podemos was founded in 2014 by Pablo Iglesias in order to address the problems of inequality, unemployment and economic malaise in Spain in the wake of the Eurozone debt crisis. (Castello, Manuel, 2015. *Networks of Outrage and Hope: Social Movements in the Internet Age*. Wiley.)

126. The seventy-four-year-old senator Bernie Sanders campaigned for the Democratic party's nomination for the United States presidential election in 2016. He initially enjoyed wide support within the liberal and white voting bloc. His socialist and populist manifesto called for universal healthcare purchased by the state, publicly funded elections, free higher education, more protectionist trade policies and a redistributive tax system that raises money for job-creating infrastructure projects. (Roberts, Dan. *The Guardian*, 12th September 2015.)

127. The former Conservative Chancellor Kenneth Clarke warned in an interview that Mr Corbyn's brand of left-

wing populism would be hard to campaign against. It was not certain he would lose an election. Clarke is quoted: "If you have another recession or if the Conservative government becomes very unpopular, he could win." (Bennett, Owen. The Huffington Post UK, 3rd August 2015.)

128. Larry Elliot in 2014 presented five warning signs that the recovery of the global economy may be an illusion – dependency on exceptionally low interest rates; a threat of a bond market crash; the risk of a housing-bubble burst or a collapse in the fracking market; climate change leading to conflicts over resources; and rising inequality leading to social unrest. (Elliott, Larry. *The Guardian*, 7th April 2014.) Seamus Milne in 2015 warned that the latest drop in the value of stocks in the Chinese financial market only underlined the fragility of the so-called recovery. He concluded that *After three decades of deregulation punctuated by financial crises and a systemic meltdown, there is every reason to fear more fallout from casino capitalism. (The Guardian,* 27th August 2015.)

129. Nicholas Watt, Patrick Wintour and Rowena Mason reported that Jeremy Corbyn faced a challenge to his authority as newly elected party leader from his own Shadow Defence Secretary, Maria Eagle, when he said at his first party conference that he would never as Prime Minister authorise the use of nuclear weapons. Corbyn and his new Shadow Chancellor, John McDonnell, were longstanding supporters of the Campaign for Nuclear Disarmament (see p. 4–5 and Reference 4 above). (*The Guardian*, 1st October 2015.)

130. John McDonnell MP was one of the dozen or so avowedly socialist MPs who worked to ensure Jeremy Corbyn's nomination in the leadership election. McDonnell made his first Labour party conference speech as Shadow Chancellor in late September 2015, stating that: "We are embarking on the immense task of changing the economic discourse in this country. We are throwing off that ridiculous charge that we are deficit deniers... we are rejecting austerity as the means to do it." (*The Guardian*, 29th September 2015.)

131. Jeremy Corbyn's core principles were outlined when he joined the race for the leadership and then reproduced in an email to supporters after his victory and before the party conference. (Jeremy Corbyn for Labour Leader info@jeremyforlabour.com. Retrieved 25th September 2015.)

132. Jeremy Hunt, the Conservative Minister for Health, in an onstage interview at the Conservative party conference in October 2015, suggested that those reliant on tax credits and benefits lacked self-respect. "If you are earning an income [£16,500] yourself you are independent and that is the first step to self-respect... It is about pathways to work, pathways to independence, self-respect and dignity." The Chancellor, George Osborne, on the same conference day, spelt out his vision of the Conservatives as the "builders" of a new Britain. (*The Guardian*, 6th October 2015.) The Prime Minister, David Cameron, presented his vision of the Conservatives as the new party of labour focused on "an all-out assault on poverty" in his closing conference speech. (*The Guardian*. 8 October 2015.) In that same

edition of the *Guardian* newspaper, Patrick Wintour and Nicholas Watt reported that new research by the Resolution Foundation, now chaired by a former Conservative minister, David Willetts, suggested that government welfare cuts introduced in the budget in order to cut the deficit would drive at least 200,000 working households into poverty under a definition that the government was abolishing.